"South Carolina is too small to be a
republic and too large to be an
insane asylum."

—James Louis Petigru

2009

The   Petigru   Review

Volume Three

South Carolina Writers Workshop
P.O. Box 7104
Columbia, SC 29202
www.myscww.org

D1307358

Editor's Note: *Word Journeys*
By Kami Kinard

I fell in love with reading as a child after discovering that words—when strung together in just the right order—created enough energy to transport me to other worlds. Words took me on great journeys! So I began trying to create my own worlds almost as soon as I learned to form letters with those fat red pencils teachers used to give us in first grade.

I've been writing for a few decades now, not always professionally, of course. And working to improve my skills through workshops, classes, conferences, and reading, reading, reading, has taught me that the best writers have one thing in common. They are able to craft their words into vehicles sturdy enough to carry others to unique destinations. This is what happens in many of the titles found in this year's issue of *The Petigru Review.*

These destinations do not have to be physical. We may be taken on an emotional journey, as we are in *The Knock*, a wonderful piece of fiction that begins with an ending and ends with a beginning. Or perhaps we travel through the thoughts of a singular personality, as in *Miz Audrey Goes to Church.*

When we start reading pieces such as these, we want to know where we will be when the story ends. We have this same compulsion when good writers share their experiences through nonfiction essays. As soon as we meet the two adorable but vicious mini-donks in *Anything for a Story*, we want to know what happens to the journalist who met them first.

When we hike out west with a father and his adult son in *Sudden Man*, we are delighted to discover that the destination the author reaches is one that many of us have reached—or will reach—without having to travel across the country.

Sometimes a journey begins and ends with the mundane, but still carries us to a new place. This occurs in a number of this year's poems. In *Plastic Jesus,* the speaker ruminates on the philosophy of lawn-ornament selection. *In Sailing Yarn*, our eyes are opened to the oceans found in puddles. And through the speaker's imagination, we're allowed to glimpse a tender death ritual that she will never glimpse in *To My Daughters Who Will Wash Me.*

Whether we ride along on the backs of words to emotional, physical, fantastic, or philosophical destinations, the perfect journey will end with last lines that do not force us to look back at the road we've just traveled, but will propel us forward. I am tempted to share some of these perfect endings with you now. But I realized along the way that I didn't want to spoil the ride for those of you prepared to embark on the third issue of *The Petigru Review.*

Thank you, members of the South Carolina Writer's Workshop, for sending your best words forward. They have paved the way to some fabulous places.

Now, turn the page. Begin the journey.

Table of Contents

Photography Credits

Betty Wilson Beamguard: 36, 54, 76, 86, 91, 140

Chaytor Chandler: title page, 10, 17, 25, 40, 118, 222

Kevin Coyle: cover, copyright page, table of contents, 41, 95, 107, 123, 145, 174, 220

Under a Good Hat
By Donna Campbell

Genevieve knows the hat is a good one as soon as she spots it, perched like an exotic bird, in the shop on Savannah's River Street. Genevieve believes in signs, and she's certain the lovely hat is the sign she's been expecting.

She waves at the wispy clerk. Genevieve thinks the child needs some meat on her bones. "Yoo-hoo! Sweetheart, let me see that hat, will you? That one . . . the lavender one with the fuzzies all over it . . . that's right . . . thank you."

The clerk stares open-mouthed, incredulous. Genevieve is well aware that she is a woman of unusual size. The girl's bad manners don't faze her. She neither understands young folks nor cares much about them. They might as well be an extraterrestrial species for all she has in common with them.

The young clerk's approval or disapproval doesn't matter to Genevieve, but Walter—well, now Walter is another matter entirely. She has had her eye on Walter since he boarded their tour bus two days ago. She thinks he may be her kind of man. Walter, who is barely two-thirds as high and a third as wide as Genevieve, is merely a mast of a man compared to her. Genevieve confidently sails through life, parting humanity with her bulk. She knows a thing or two about men, especially the thin, retiring ones, who are drawn to a woman like her. It's as if she is an iron bulwark, strong and secure, and more than one man, his heart magnetized by her unusual charms, has found himself clamped to her.

Genevieve navigates the narrow aisle of bric-a-brac that tourists crave until she stands before a painted Cheshire cat whose belly holds a mirror. She grins at her reflection as she twists the incredible lavender hat around her substantial head. She turns her head left, then right, adjusting the hat's high crown and wide brim. It is the color of wisteria and appears to be spun from lavender steel wool. Genevieve is pleased.

"Ring it up, sweetie! Don't bother to wrap it, just take off the tag." She pays for it in cash, extracting her money purse from the crevasse between her breasts. Genevieve is comfortable with her large bosom, unlike some women she knows. It has been the demise of more than one good man, swallowing him up like a doomed mountaineer. The clerk's shock does not register with Genevieve as she extracts her money. She doesn't notice how the girl hesitates to take the extended twenties, holding them gingerly with her manicured nails as if the money is toxic.

All Genevieve cares about is the beautiful hat and how it makes her eyes turn a deeper shade of gray and how it sits on her coiffed curls jauntily, confirming her belief that it is a good sign. Walter will surely appreciate a woman who wears a hat like this lavender one. It is a fine color for her.

Genevieve is definitely a hat woman. She believes women fall into two groups—those who wear a hat to fend off rain or sun, and those like her who know that under a good hat, a woman becomes something more. She believes there is magic in a woman who walks through life under a good hat, and the lavender one is just such a hat.

She wanders out into the September warmth. The rest of her tour companions, including Walter, are off mewing and mooing over the famous house that had been in that movie. She isn't interested in old houses. She strolls along the waterfront, oblivious to the heads she turns as she makes her way down the sidewalk like some regal old steamboat, hugging the cement channel, full steam ahead, claiming her right of way. More than one astonished pedestrian is forced back against a shop wall, yielding to her bulk.

Before reaching the end of the waterfront, she stops at a tiny sidewalk stand and buys herself lemonade and a chili dog.

The milk-chocolate man behind the narrow, grease-speckled counter grins at her, flashing gold from a lower molar, a ray of dental sunshine. "You want onions and relish on that? Don't worry. No charge for 'em."

"Sure, now, why not." Genevieve projects the full radiance of her own smile onto the little man, reaching down deep into the crevice of her bosom to extract her purse.

He stacks pungent onions and relish precariously onto the chilidog. He does not take his eyes away from the scene before him—Genevieve retrieving her money purse from her cleavage. He leans toward her. His nostrils flare slightly. "Ma'am, you sure do smell nice! That's some fine perfume. Hope you won't take offense at me saying so."

Genevieve smiles. "Well, now, I don't mind at all. I don't never turn down a compliment." She is fond of strong perfume, dabbing it on every morning under each voluminous breast, dispatching waves of fragrance that can make the right man desire to drown in her ocean of scented flesh.

The little man mops his brow with a dishtowel. Genevieve thinks he looks like a rabbit, brown and quick in his movements. For a moment, she imagines he's a chocolate Easter bunny, shiny and slick, melting in the heat.

He hands her the overloaded hotdog and says, "Nice hat. Nice color."

"Well, thank you. Nothing makes a woman more than a good hat."

"Ain't that the truth, ma'am. You have a good day now."

Genevieve lowers herself onto a bench overlooking the river. She watches a paddlewheel excursion boat waddle across the wakes thrown up by careless boaters. Walter sits on Genevieve's mind much as the hat now sits on her head. Each day he's taken the seat across the aisle from her on the Everyman Tours bus. He isn't much of a talker, which is a good sign. She has enough to say for two people. The quiet ones don't mind a woman like her who can fill the emptiness between their sparse words. The small ones, like Walter, don't mind that she fills the physical space they leave empty. Genevieve is good at completing an incomplete man.

Daintily, she consumes the hotdog. She is impressively delicate, fastidiously wiping her plump hands each time she takes a bite. Soon, the entire meal is nothing more than a pleasant memory and a wad of soiled napkins. Genevieve cleans her teeth with a few swipes of her pink tongue. She hoists her bulk up and wanders toward the rubbish container, then notices the surly girl sitting a bench away, staring at her. The two females are exact opposites—Genevieve's impressive bulk crowned by the incredible lavender hat and the scrawniness of the girl, dressed in fake black leather and studded with piercings so that she looks like an emaciated orange stuck all over with cloves. The teenager stares at her, wary, scowling.

The girl speaks, spitting and spewing like a feral cat. "Gawd . . . gawddd . . . that is the most gruesome hat I've ever seen, and you are the most gruesome woman I've ever met."

Genevieve is curious but otherwise unmoved by the venomous creature. She tips her head a bit higher, balances the lavender hat regally on her head, and studies the awful child sitting across from her. Genevieve decides the girl can't be more than 15 or 16.

"Guess that's just your opinion, girl. It don't much matter to me what you think or you don't think. Anyway, how come you done made your face look like a barbed-wire fence? Don't those things hurt? How in heaven would you ever get a man to kiss you with those lips of yours? Hang, you could get yourself caught up on his bridgework and you'd have to call nine-one-one to get you sprung! Now, that would be embarrassing!"

The feral child leans forward, back bowing, as if ready to spring. "I'll tell you what's embarrassing—you are, you and that damned ugly hat. Gawddd . . . that hat looks like somebody dropped a giant blueberry on your head, and it got stuck in your brain. Nobody but a fat, old woman like you would be dumb enough to wear a hat like that."

"Well, now, your mama would be awfully proud of manners like yours, wouldn't she? What cause do you have to be so nasty on a nice September day? You know your problem? I bet you done already figured out no man's going to look twice at a scrawny, underfed thing like you. I know you kids think a man won't love you unless you look like a fence pole, all straight lines and no curves. But you got a lot to learn. I ain't taking no offense at your bad manners. You're young and going through your mean stage. Shoot, I wouldn't be too happy, either, if I saw myself looking like you in the mirror when I passed. But what you need, girl, is to ditch those things that make you look like a dern television antenna and throw away those black clothes and get yourself something girly. You'd look good in fuchsia. You got the right coloring, and get yourself a good hat. You ain't never too young to wear a good hat."

Genevieve doesn't let the girl have the last word. She turns and sails back up River Street, resisting the temptation to look back, sensing that her words have landed like poop from a seagull. What kind of mother lets her child dress that way? If the girl hadn't been quite so nasty, she might have offered to buy the child a good meal. No meat on the bones at all. Maybe she has one of those eating disorders Genevieve has heard about on Oprah. A pity—the child's too young to know the powerful draw that warm, soft flesh has on a man when the night is cold or when he wakes from a nightmare he'd just as soon forget. The girl has a lot to learn.

Genevieve shakes off the unpleasant encounter quickly, amusing herself with window-shopping and people-watching. She works her way up the avenue lined with expensive shops and exclusive restaurants and stops at one, studying the menu in the little glass window beside the entrance. She contemplates entering. The dessert menu is especially tempting, but, marking the time on a clock in the jewelry-store window next door, she rejects the temptation. She has to keep a steady pace if she expects to reach the bus waiting at the Visitor's Center in time to save a seat across from her for Walter. She comforts herself with a promise to buy fudge and some chocolate-covered raisins for Walter at the sweet shop up the block.

Genevieve steps aside smartly as the restaurant door suddenly swings open, disgorging two stylishly dressed ladies draped in expensive jewelry.

Genevieve knows the type: country club women. She hangs back for a moment and watches them totter up the sidewalk on their absurdly expensive heels. She shakes her head in disgust when she sees them dart across the avenue to avoid a crippled old street musician who offers to play them a song on his banjo. Both women toss the old man looks of aversion over their shoulders and disappear into one of the elegant boutiques lining the avenue.

Genevieve drifts up the street until she is even with the old man. "Can you play 'Tennessee Waltz' on that thing?"

He grins at her and takes up his instrument. The little man plucks loss and longing out of the battered banjo. Broken crystal notes linger in the humid Savannah air. The melancholy chords wrap around Genevieve and a tear wells up in her eye. She is a fool for the old ballads.

"You sure know how to wring a song out of that banjo." She dips her hand into the well of her bosom and draws up a $10 bill. She wedges it carefully into the old man's coffee can. The grizzled musician's eyes linger on the expanse of Genevieve. "Why, ma'am, God bless you and Jesus save you. That is a fine hat you're wearing, fit for a good woman like yourself. You have a blessed day, now, you hear?"

"Well, thank you, I intend to. Tootle-loo."

She continues her path up the sidewalk, jiggling a bit more lively as she hears the man strike up the chorus to "Old Susannah." She draws near the sweet shop and carefully crosses the avenue at the pedestrian walkway. She reckons she'll buy a pound box of fudge, the kind where you choose three flavors—maybe praline, milk chocolate, and rocky road. That seems about right. She hasn't quite made up her mind how much raisins to buy Walter. Maybe half a pound? She doesn't want him to think she's a spendthrift, though two deceased husbands have left her well fixed.

She pushes her way through the brightly decorated door of the sweet shop and gives a "humph" of displeasure when she sees the two elegantly dressed women who so recently displayed their lack of Christian charity. A young clerk offers each woman samples of chocolate-covered strawberries—dark ones, milk-chocolate ones, white-chocolate ones.

The skinny woman addresses her slightly younger companion. "What do you think, Lorraine . . . the milk chocolate is to die for, but the white chocolate is sooo much more cosmopolitan, don't you think? After all, it is supposed to be high tea. Run-of-the punch and cookies won't do."

"Oh, I couldn't agree more. They're exactly the right touch."

The young clerk sheepishly informs them that the white-chocolate strawberries are rather more expensive than the others, a full dollar more a pound, and since the ladies are planning to order eight dozen for the St. Paul's Women's Circle tea, perhaps they may want to consider the milk-chocolate ones instead.

The two ladies pause. The skinny one gives her companion a "What do you think?" look, then, giggling, airily waves her jeweled hand and says, "Oh, go ahead. What does it matter? It's just money."

Genevieve notes all of this as she circles unseen around the cases of hand-dipped confections. She lingers in front of the fudge counter, mulling over the merits of rocky road versus cashew caramel. Accidentally, she brushes a small wind chime on display. The two women and the clerk look up, noticing Genevieve. The skinny one rolls her eyes upward and tilts her head toward her friend. The women bend their heads together over the chocolate-covered strawberries and twitter, surfacing momentarily to give Genevieve a withering look.

Genevieve resolves to ignore them. As with the feral child, she doesn't care what folks think of her. She certainly doesn't think much of the condescending, smirking women.

But the skinny one isn't done with Genevieve yet. "Skinny" whispers in a voice loud enough for Genevieve to hear. "You'd think anyone that fat would be too embarrassed to waddle into a candy store for all the world to see. Anyone with self-esteem that low and no self-discipline should stay home and hide."

Genevieve's head snaps up, precariously tilting the lavender hat on her head. Her forbearance is not boundless. The skinny woman has pushed beyond its limits. Genevieve stares down the skinny one. "Well, now, missy, I may be heavy in the trunk, but at least I ain't a cheap, scrawny pretense of a Christian woman."

The young clerk behind the counter steps carefully away from the women, looking frantically around to see if anyone else is witnessing the unfolding fracas. She moves as far away as she can from the ruffled Genevieve and the unpleasant skinny woman.

"I beg your pardon! How dare you!" exclaims the skinny one.

"How dare me? How dare you walk by that poor old man out there with his banjo and not even have the charity to toss him the loose change in your purse? Humph, but you got enough nerve to spend a ridiculous amount on those strawberries for your rich, snooty friends that sure don't need nobody to buy 'em any food. And another thing while you got me going. Who gave you the right to decide that a woman with a little weight on her is too ugly to be seen in public? It seems to me the Bible says that we're all created in God's image—white, yeller, black, skinny, and fat like me—all of us, so I guess that means God must be fat, too, at least some of the time. So if plump's good enough for God, it's good enough for me. Anyway, for all you or me know, God might be a fat, happy woman, big enough to take care of the whole universe. Ain't nothing in the Bible says for sure he's a skinny old man. So you might want to think next time before you decide to insult one of God's children.

"You there, yes, you girl. Pack me up a pound of that fudge in one of them variety boxes, please—make it praline, milk chocolate, and rocky road and give me a half-pound of them chocolate-covered raisins—and make it fast if you can."

"Now you just wait one minute, you old sow!" Genevieve's heated retorts have melted away any pretense of good breeding from the skinny woman. "If you want to quote the Bible, I'd remind you that we're instructed to treat our bodies as temples of God, and yours is certainly in a state of disgrace!" The woman's thin skin barely contains the bulging blood vessels that now pulse dangerously on each side of her brow.

Genevieve retrieves her money from its secret hiding place—an action noted by Lorraine, the younger companion, who looks pale and panicked. Genevieve counters, "Well, that's true. It does say our bodies are temples of God. The way I see it is that God blessed me with a temple bigger and grander than your scrawny one. Now I ain't got no more time for the unchristian likes of you and your pale-as-a-ghost friend over there. If you don't mind, miss, can you wrap up that candy for me and take this money? I got a bus to catch."

The young clerk scrambles to complete the sale and watches, mouth agape, as Genevieve tugs open the door and glides into the warm afternoon, leaving the stunned women in her wake.

Without further incident, Genevieve reaches the tour bus that sits baking in the sun. She knocks on the door and rouses the dozing driver. Groggily, he lets her board. She offers him some fudge.

"Thanks . . . looks good. I think I will."

Genevieve works a chunk of milk chocolate free in the box and holds it out for the man. The driver takes it and looks up at the hat sitting regally on the large woman's head. "Fine hat you got there. Always like a good hat on a woman."

"Well, do you now? Thank you. I'm right partial to hats."

She maneuvers her way almost to the back of the bus, just a few rows away from the toilet. It is the seat she favors—close enough for convenience but not too close.

She waits patiently as the other passengers trickle back from their sightseeing day. Every few minutes, she pokes a little plastic knife into a mound of fudge and dislodges a small sliver, then daintily brings it to her mouth and deposits it on the tip of her tongue. She lets it linger there, content in the pleasure of its melting sweetness. Her mind is untroubled; her conscience is clear.

When she sees Walter pop up from the bus steps like the small, bald-headed weasel he resembles, she readies the bag of chocolate-covered raisins. Just before Walter reaches her, she dangles the bag from her hand the way she'd hold out a treat for a favorite dog. "I brought you something from the sweet shop. Thought you might like 'em . . . chocolate-covered raisins."

This stops Walter in his tracks. He swings himself into the seat across from the one Genevieve so amply fills. He gives her a timid smile. Genevieve thinks he makes good eye contact, thinks that's another good sign. She flashes him a generous smile.

Walter reaches out and takes the raisins from her. "Thank you . . . uh . . ."

"Genevieve . . . name's Genevieve. Thought you looked like a chocolate-covered raisin man. Me, I like my fudge."

"Yes, how 'bout that. These raisins are my favorite." He takes a good look at Genevieve, then points at her head. "I must say, that's quite a hat you're wearing. I always admire a woman who wears a hat well, and you sure do wear that one just fine."

"Thank you. I've always appreciated a man who knows enough to appreciate a woman's hat. Want to try this fudge? It's good."

"Well, now. I do. I'd like that."

Anything for a Story
By Betty Wilson Beamguard

My friend Audrey knew I'd done magazine features and asked if I'd write about her mini-donks for *Miniature Donkey Talk*. "They're so cute," she said. "You can't help but love 'em."

I promised to interview them and drove over to find her at the donkey pen with her four-year-old granddaughter Kenzie. They introduced me to Bandit, white with black markings, and Pancho, taupe with a black cross on his back. The little fellows poked their muzzles over the fence.

"How precious." I reached to pet them.

"Watch out. They bite."

I withdrew my hand and Audrey handed me a copy of the magazine. While I thumbed through looking at smiling people hugging burros, Kenzie offered Bandit a Nicker Biscuit and leaned toward his nose with her lips puckered. I whipped out my camera.

"We didn't know a thing about donkeys when we got them," Audrey said. "The boys are a lot cheaper and we didn't know better than to buy two males. The older they got, the more they fought until we were scared they'd kill each other, so we had them neutered. But they're still mean."

Mean? How could she call those sweet babies mean? I coughed and stepped back as Kenzie patted Pancho's neck, beating out a cloud of dust.

"They have a dust wallow down at the foot of the hill," Audrey explained.

I eyed the roomy pasture. "I need pictures without the fence. Can you get them out in the open?"

"They won't leave the fence as long as we're here."

"Then I need to go inside the pen."

"Oh no, I never go in there. They kick. They're just playing, but it'd probably break your leg."

I thought, forget this. They wouldn't run a piece about these little devils. The people who pay for ads to sell their donkeys and related products would not appreciate negative press. Every article has to be ridiculously positive.

"We could drive the golf cart in," Audrey suggested.

That sounded safe, so I agreed to try it. I eased open the gate while she edged forward in the cart. Problem was, the gate caught on a section of fence wire that lay on the ground. Pancho bolted for the opening. I struck an extreme yoga pose, balancing on one foot with the other stuck in Pancho's face while I reached through the gate to move the wire.

I swung the gate open just enough for the cart. Audrey drove in, leaving me to face the wee beasties, who now stood side by side with "Charge!" written on their furry faces. They shot forward. I threw up my hands and yelled. They skidded to a stop. I slammed the gate, hooked the chain over the nail, and raced for the cart with donkeys hot on my heels.

I jumped into the golf cart before they caught up, but my relief was short-lived. That imp Pancho stuck his head in and nipped my thigh, and we couldn't get them to leave. I wanted pictures with the woods in the background; instead, I was snapping close-ups of muzzles.

We tried sitting perfectly still, hoping they'd lose interest and wander off, but with the feed bucket on the back of the cart, that ploy failed. Next I hopped out and Audrey buzzed off. They headed after Audrey, but then noticed me standing in the open and here they came. I took off in a dead run, waving my camera as I yelled for her to stop. During the next half hour, I got more exercise than I usually get in a week. When I'd had all the fun I could stand, we made our escape.

The pictures are all either way too close or too distant. Each time the critters headed my way, I fled before they got close enough for a good shot, but I cropped them and have some that are usable. My favorite shows Pancho storming up the hill after a dust bath, his eyes glowing an eerie green.

Now I'm trying to come up with something nice to write about Pancho and Bandit to get them into the mini-donk magazine. It won't be easy.

Wash
By Kathryn Etters Lovatt

Under this sun, the ghost of my grandmother appears.
My mother follows, a shimmer in her wake.
The two stand ankle-deep in nettles and wicker baskets.
Their teeth are clothespins.

They move down the line in unison,
pitching the tails of bleached sheets skyward;
a snatch of their wrists seeds the day with billow.
For this second, the world is white percale and dreams.

I lay unborn beneath a skein of mimosa and honeybees.
I wait for spoons of gone-to-sugar honey, berries.
for tender greens, the smell of chicken scratch,
for the blue sky, two clouds and a slight wind.

My mothers will fetch me once they're done.
They will finish here and come and lift
the thought of me into the folds of their aprons
They will take me home.

Even now, their pocket charms sing in my ear:
river rock, pulley-bone,
blade and spoon.
Nothing has begun yet, and nothing is over.

The Knock
By Kim Catanzarite

The shower runs rivulets down my back. I am trying to wake up, and yet my eyes close. I have been sleeping too much. And standing under this shower. Entire days have slithered down this drain.

I turn the faucet, wrap myself in a towel, then startle when I see him stooped over the sink. He is brushing his teeth. I do not disturb, instead apply lotion to my legs. A layer of deodorant under each arm. It's his presence that makes me aware of the channels between my ribs. The fact that I am diminishing.

And then he is gone. He does that. Brushes and goes. No goodbye. No see you tonight. Off to work. Focused, engrossed.

I make the bed. My side is easy to fix. Pull the wrinkles out of the bottom. Tug up the blankets, freshen the hospital fold, then run my hand over his side. Smooth.

For breakfast, I pull out the bread for toast. A spoon clangs a bowl behind me and a shiver tunes my spine. He is there. At the table. Eating cereal. Reading the paper.

I say, "To what do I owe this pleasure?"

He reads on. Eats on. It has been months since he has eaten at this table.

"Joining me for breakfast?"

He reaches for a glass of orange juice glowing like the sun, and I cringe, thinking *acidity* and the hole in his stomach. He smiles and gulps, eyes sparkling like the golden drops that linger in the corners of his mouth.

My toast pops. I spread a layer of butter, fill a glass with water. "Don't you disappear before I get over there."

He opens the real-estate section.

I pull out a chair. "Work, work, work. No rest 'til you're dead, right?"

"I *am* dead," he says.

The happiness drops from my face, and he looks up from his reading. "You got the money. That's good."

"It came yesterday."

He crunches on bacon. "What now? Will you get a job?"

I grimace. "Only if I can do it from the couch."

He sits back, beaming disappointment. "You promised to stay positive."

"If you could come around more often, I wouldn't mind so much."

He pierces a piece of ham, tops it with a wedge of potato. His plate is an amalgamation of breakfast delights: eggs, pancakes, ham steak, donuts. I feel the stir of hunger in my throat. He lifts an English muffin, smothers it with jam. He has not eaten like this in years, I cannot recall our last Sunday at the Cozy Corner.

"You don't come by enough," I say.

He swallows. "You stopped praying."

I remember that I want to tell him I'm sorry. Not for not praying, but for other things. "I used to complain that I did all the work around here. But now I see that yard work really *is* hard. And remembering the garbage and getting the recycles out every other week. I didn't mean it when I said I'd divorce you if you didn't pull your own weight. . . ."

He is into the cheddar omelet, its gooey insides oozing onto the plate.

"I wouldn't mind it so much if you'd come around more often."

Something outside distracts him. He pulls back the curtain, recognizes something or someone. I see nothing. No one. The crape myrtle waves a wiry branch.

"These visits have to stop," he says. "You can't understand, so don't try."

"But I'm devastated, and you're eating sausage and butter."

He scoops scrambled eggs onto a raft of rye toast and floats it into his mouth. "I've got things to do," he says, chewing.

And to eat, I think, as I feel him pull back, his presence diminishing.

"Don't go. I'll take back every unkind thing I ever said. Every thought, every complaint."

"It's not about that stuff, Gloria." He wipes his mouth with his napkin. He was always a handsome man. Dignified even in the end. Cancer had nothing on him. "You're young. You should eat more."

"Forty-five is *not* young."

He gives me one of his fatherly stares. "Now listen, when I leave, there's going to be a knock at the door. Answer it, OK? Don't hide, Gloria."

I pull my robe together at the neck.

"It's important that you answer the door, OK hon?"

I nod. He reaches for salt, his napkin wafting like a feather to the floor by my feet. I stretch to pick it up.

I say, "Who's going to be there?"

I'm too late. He and his plate are gone.

At the end, when he resembled an anorexic, he said, "You'll find someone better . . . or at least more attractive." To which I responded: "Did I ever tell you how much I love your bones?"

If Bobby is sending someone my way, if that someone is going to knock at my door, I decide I should probably be dressed. I've been living in my robe for some time now, long enough for the contents of my closet to appear strange, for my jeans to suit some other, larger body. I slide into a pair nonetheless, and a cotton knit top Bobby's mother gave me last Christmas. In the living room, I toss away pillows to make room on the couch. My legs are crossed, foot bobbing, I wait for the knock. I get up, I pace. That's when I notice the mantle, how it's lost under a snow-covering of dust—enough to glide a sled over. I rush down the hall, grab a hand towel and furniture polish. I'm speed-cleaning now, disrupting snowdrifts and ushering dirty cups, toast crusts, and wadded Kleenex into the appropriate receptacles. I fill the dishwasher, load the clothes washer, raise the blinds. I open the window and the house gasps for air. A profusion of light outs an army of dirt devils converged at the baseboard. The vacuum hurts my ears, but it's a necessary evil. When I'm done, I look in the mirror. The color is coming back.

A knock at the door. My lethargy flinches, then sinks back into soft fibers. Cushy couch pillows and blanket. My groggy mind, accustomed to oblivion, slides backward into contented snores. Then another knock. *Answer it, OK? Don't hide, Gloria.* I force myself up, endure the head rush. It could be the "someone better." I rub my eyes. Pull open the door. The house inhales. Little girl. Green outfit like a leprechaun. Folder, pen. "Would you like to buy cookies?" Beside the crape myrtle, a woman stands with her arms folded over her chest.

"That's it?"

The leprechaun shrugs. I stoop to one knee. Order three boxes. She can't be it. I try to think of one way cookies might change my life for the better.

For a year, I answer every knock at my door. Newspaper boys, politicians, lawn guys, religious fanatics, cleaning women looking for dirty houses (mine no longer qualifies), a neighbor in need of a dog-walker. None of them make a difference in my life. Still, I hope. I answer. I even agree to walk the dog.

One rainy evening, a man emerges from the shadows, drenched from head to foot. It's late for social visits so I have second thoughts, but then Bobby's *Don't hide!* rings in my ears. I figure it may be the "someone better" in disguise. I invite him and his cloud-gray trench into the foyer. He says he knew my husband, that he's sorry for my loss. Then he eyes the place. "Nice house. So clean."

"I'm expecting someone. What did you say your name was?"

"Jackie." He says. "Kennedy."

I wonder if it's a joke or a lie. I gesture toward the kitchen, thinking my husband better be watching, guardian-angel style.

"Reason I'm here," Jackie says, his wet hair like a swim cap over his skull, "is I figure a respectable guy like Bob must have had life insurance."

Oh, so he's here to rob me, or maybe kill me. Maybe that's why Bobby insisted I answer the door. So when this guy came along, he could put me out of my misery, and I could join Bobby in heaven. The thing is, I don't want to die. Not so long ago, I thought I wouldn't mind it so much, but now I can see I'm not ready to go.

"Are you OK?" he asks.

I unclench my hands, look at him warily.

He cocks his head, his face gray and sad. "I just thought you might want to earn some cash. I'm doing this business-venture thing, not sure you've heard about it. You make a small investment at the start, then recruit other people to—"

I make a snorting sound, more as an expression of relief than mockery, but he doesn't know that.

"It's not a scam," he says.

I pat his back, start him toward the door. "Thanks for stopping by."

Just before he leaves, I tell him to wait. I go back for the box of Girl Scout cookies I never opened, the ones with the nuts I don't care for. I hand it to him. "Take care."

Once he's gone, it occurs to me that my house *is* very clean, and when it's not raining, it's bright, too. And I'm relatively happy, which is probably why Bobby told me to answer the knock at the door. That Sneaky Pete just wanted to get me off the couch.

And then I feel a bit of gloom when I realize "someone better" probably isn't coming to save me.

The next day, I get out and search for a job. Volunteer because I don't need money. What I need is a reason to stay off the couch. And people who make me feel like the relatively young person I am. Nursing homes do that well.

On the anniversary of my third month of ice chips and reading books out loud, I'm driving along when I pass an accident on the side of the road. It's just a fender-bender but it crosses my mind that I can do CPR if someone needs saving—I

got certified the week before. I pass the Cozy Corner, where Bobby and I used to gorge on pancakes and cheddar omelets before his life became all about what he couldn't eat. The parking lot at the nursing home is empty because I'm always early and only one or two of the oldies retains the right to drive. I gather my sweater, my purse. My glasses slip to the floor, so I reach for them. And then I startle at a sharp knock on the window.

Dr. Larson peers at me through the glass. Handsome Dr. Larson. I press a button. The window goes down.

"You hungry?" he asks, checking his watch. "You want to eat?"

You answer that door, Gloria. Don't hide!

I say, "Um, sure."

He waves me out of the car. "I'll drive," he says. "We've got plenty of time."

To My Daughters, Who Will Dress Me
By Sally Arango Renata

Wash me. You will use warm water
to warm my flesh, to soothe me, to soothe you.

You will touch my hair because
it doesn't turn cold, because it is still growing.

My hand reached for the temperate
grey of my mother's hair, after she was gone.
I should have kept a lock.

Holding my hair, you will remember
your children braiding small strands,
covering my head with colored barrettes.
You will wonder who has that picture now,
my head covered in barrettes.

As you wash, somewhere between my shoulders
and breasts your pain will ease.
You'll recall how I lived twenty lifetimes.

It will be then that you'll wish I was
prepared for my journey: that my cuticles
were trimmed, toenails painted,
the paint scraped from under my fingernails . . .

But then that wasn't me. I wasn't manicured.
I wore Birkenstocks, absorbing earth
from the garden into my heels, between my toes.
Freckles of paint dotted my hands,
I was not manicured.

There is a box with a sari in the closet.
I opened the gift, spreading seven yards
of silk laced with golden thread across
the living-room floor and I knew
it would dress me in death.

I saw green cover my head,
wrap closely around my shoulders.
In life I'd wear the vibrancy of red,
but green springs from darkened soil.

I'll have no shoes, nothing but the delicate
silken shroud and a ring on my finger,
golden curves of Arabic that announce:

I come forth from God, and return unto Him,
the Merciful, the Compassionate.

A Sudden Man
By Bob Strother

We were headed north to Silverton, Colorado, surrounded as far as the eye could see by the southern Rockies of the San Juan National Forest. Even in the middle of July, patches of snow still decorated the highest peaks. My son, Matt, seemed relaxed behind the wheel as he navigated the beautiful but circuitous mountain road. He pointed through the windshield to a mountainside alive with silvery quaking aspens.

"They're like jazz hands," he said, lifting one hand from the steering wheel to give me a demonstration. The splay-fingered shimmering of his hand brought to mind Al Jolson in *The Jazz Singer*, but Matt, just over 30, would likely cite a more recent reference. "They're the world's largest living organisms, you know."

"What are?" I asked.

"Aspen groves—they have a common root system. There's one in Utah some people say is eighty thousand years old."

I looked over at him and thought how our roles had become reversed over the years. I'd taught him to swim and play tennis; now here he was explaining scientific organisms to me. It also reminded me how little I really knew him—something I hoped to remedy by walking in his world.

I'd come west to go camping, biking, and hiking with my son—just him and me—in the wilds of Colorado, where men were men and cargo shorts were actually functional. The first night we'd spent in Durango, and met the loquacious Cowboy Bruce, who told us about riding his Harley around the country and his recent brain aneurysm.

"I see life from a whole new perspective now," Bruce said. "If I'm going out, I want it to be in a blaze of glory."

"Which way are you headed?" Matt asked.

The cowboy leaned back against the bar, his paunch straining against the pearl-studded closures of his yoked shirt. He took another pull from a longneck Bud. "East."

Matt looked at me and grinned. "Good," he said.

We were traveling north.

.....

On Tuesday evening, we arrived at the campground in Crested Butte, and pitched our tent beside the banks of the Slate River, near the U-Be-Joyful trailhead. The following morning, Matt, an experienced outdoorsman, made coffee and oatmeal for breakfast. Surprisingly, the gruel-like stuff that gagged me as a child became ambrosia in the crisp mountain air. We rode our bikes 12 miles that day, and hiked another six. Our reward was dinner in town at Calypso's—ribs and bratwurst and Negra Modelo, the best beer I'd ever tasted.

The following morning, we forded the river and hiked 10 miles up Gunnison Mountain. Matt's camera had a timer, and we were able to capture our likenesses—scruffy and unwashed though we were—with majestic snow-capped peaks in the distance. Back in camp, my legs were wobbly, but I had persevered. And if Matt had been taking it easy on me, he was gracious enough not to let it show. It began to rain after we finished lunch, so we broke camp and headed for Montrose, a welcome shower, and fish and chips at Smuggler's.

.....

The next stop on our odyssey was Telluride, where the *nouveau riche* vacation and marauding bears roam the town during the wee hours, pillaging trash cans on Main Street. We stayed at the New Sheraton Hotel and roamed the streets ourselves, searching for eclectic bars and *haute cuisine*. Matt pointed out a 40-something female while we were having lunch. She wore a lavender wind suit, a matching bandana twisted around her Chuck Norris hairdo, and a martini in her left hand.

"Telluride active-wear," Matt informed me. "Probably drives an Escalade."

I nodded. It's always good to have a tour guide to define the local color. Later in the day, we sat in the bar at The New Sheraton and speculated on the secret lives of bartenders. Ours was buxom, blonde, and interestingly tattooed.

That night, over fried calamari, we discussed his plans to abandon his teaching career and work alongside his wife in her highly lucrative photography business. His arguments were logical and practical from a financial standpoint, but when he spoke of his students, his eyes took on a glow that no camera would ever be able to capture.

"I try to teach them to become politically aware," he said. "To understand the conservative and liberal biases of the

different media, and to make their own decisions, rather than just slipping into their parents' beliefs."

I watched his face, felt the conviction of his words, and thought to myself what a loss his leaving would mean for the educational community.

.....

After two nights in Telluride, we packed up and began our trek back to Matt's home in Flagstaff. We had a sandwich on the road, and stopped occasionally for fuel and restroom breaks. At one gas station, I went inside for a moment and came back out to see an older Native American man talking to Matt by the car. The man left as I approached.

"What was that?" I asked.

"He needed gas money," Matt said. "I gave him ten dollars."

It was not the first time I realized how much his capacity for compassion far exceeded my own.

Along the highway, bands of slender conifers marched up the mountainsides like warriors laying siege to a castle. Then the mountains became hills, and the Painted Desert opened up before us like a vast, multi-colored canvas. I sat in the passenger seat of the car like a giant sponge, listening to my son's collection of music, trying to soak up his essence.

.....

We watch them go out into the world, these sudden men and women who last year were toddlers curled around our legs, who last month dove from the high board for the first time, or who last week finally beat us at tennis. And

sometimes—either because of us or in
spite of us—they become excellent.

Author's Note: Less than a month after our trip, Matt and his wife discovered they were going to have a child. As a result, he decided to continue teaching, and re-newed his contract that fall. I hope he stays with it. I also hope that someday his son—my grandson—will find a teacher just like his father.

Plastic Jesus
By Trilby Plants

so, I'm sittin on the front step with my friend Yvonne
Lordy it's hot
and she's wearin this teeny little tube top
that her mama said she ought to be ashamed to wear in public
but Yvonne's skinny so nobody'd prob'ly notice if it did fall down

well the sweat's pourin offa me and we're drinkin beer
and bitchin 'bout how long the grass is
but the mower croaked so we can't do nothin 'bout that

we're watchin them windmills Yvonne's mama put in the yard
only they ain't movin cuz the wind died—
tornado weather the TV says

I says to Yvonne
        how come you got that there truck
        up on cement blocks

and she goes
        cuz it don't got tars

and I go
        and why you got that there plastic Jesus
        next to the lady bendin' over
        with her bloomers showin'

and she goes
        cuz Mama believes

now Jesus didn't stop Yvonne's brother
from gettin' blowed up in Eye-raq
so I wonder if plastic Jesus ain't a lot like
pink flamingos and ducks and fat ladies bendin' over
with their drawers hangin' out—
just a buncha junk clutterin' up the yard

but Yvonne's mama believes
so I guess plastic Jesus is better
than a truck on blocks

Satan's Lingerie
By Valerie Keiser Norris

The sight of all those dainty scraps of lace and satin and silk nearly brought Sheila to her knees. Surreptitiously, she touched a bra cup made of fabric so fragile that angels must have woven it in heaven. The matching panties were so sheer. . . . She straightened, her face scarlet, her entire body suffused with heat. Anyone wearing those would have no secrets.

Darting little glances here and there, Sheila draped the panties across her fingers to gauge the filmy substance. You could nearly read palms through it. Not that she would; palm-reading was as sinful as horoscopes.

A bit of lace caught her eye and soon she was wrist-deep in a stack of white lace teddies. From behind the stack stood a mannequin modeling the teddy with long white stockings, nipples clearly visible through the material. Sheila had an image of a bride dressed in the teddy and stockings, complete with veil, bouquet, and high heels. Who needed a wedding gown?

"May I help you?"

The voice at her elbow shocked Sheila. She dropped the gossamer fabrics and pulled her hands tight behind her, her heart crashing about like a wild bird trapped in a house. "I'm, umm, I was just looking," she stammered. *The salesclerk will think I'm a shoplifter,* she thought. *I'll be arrested and everyone will think I was stealing racy underwear instead of going to the "Just Jesus and Me" seminar like I was supposed to. My one time away from home, and I've ruined my life. Pastor Wittles is right—the world is a seductress. Step one foot in it alone and you'll be lost.*

But the salesclerk, a well-polished middleaged woman, acted as if there were nothing unusual in a 33-year-old woman blushing and stammering and hiding her hands behind her back. "These are lovely, aren't they?" The clerk brushed the lace with a beautiful hand, the nails shaped and polished a deep burgundy, gold bracelets glittering on her wrist.

Sheila wondered how you came to have a wrist like that, slender and pretty, not bony and angular. Her breath came in short gasps, and she could manage only a choked whisper. "Lovely."

The clerk held up a teddy and glanced from it to Sheila. "This looks to be your size. Would you like to try on anything else with it? Maybe one of these sets?" She motioned to the sheer bras and panties Sheila had noticed first.

"Oh, no, I couldn't—"

The woman acted as if she didn't hear. "Wearing fine lingerie is like a wonderful secret, don't you agree? All day I feel beautiful, knowing I'm wearing the loveliest garments I've ever seen. And no one knows but me." She stroked and fondled, gently draping items over her wrist and letting them glide over, almost playing with the lingerie.

"Yes," Sheila said softly, not sure what she was agreeing with: "Yes, I'll try them," or "Yes, I'd feel beautiful," or "Yes, let me buy everything."

The clerk understood. "Let's try these, shall we? And perhaps these. And with your coloring, oh, yes, that's marvelous."

Soon Sheila was installed in a changing room with a stack of underthings she could never wear. The thought of her mother, Miss Eva, brought Sheila back to reality. She had her hand on the doorknob, ready to escape, when the saleslady knocked. Sheila opened the door to temptation.

The woman leaned in and said in a conspiratorial whisper, "I find that clothes fit better if I line my brassieres with these. They give a bit more—definition." She held out a package of what looked like the gel pads Sheila's mother used in the heels of her sensible shoes. The clerk slipped out.

Stuff her bras? The pastor hadn't ever specifically mentioned it—although he had quite a detailed list—but Sheila was certain sin was involved somehow. She poked at the gel sacks and then cupped one in her hand. *Oh. My.*

Just trying it on wouldn't be a sin, would it? No one would see it, she wouldn't be an occasion of sin for anyone else. What could it hurt? Before she could come up with a list, she slipped off her cardigan sweater and blouse. Hands trembling, she removed the bra that was most recent in a line of plain, durable foundation garments designed to constrict movement and disguise their contents. Avoiding looking at any of the three mirrors reflecting her half-naked image, she hooked the sheer bra in front, swiveled it around, and slid her arms inside the straps. Still looking down, she put the little sacks in her bra and shifted things about.

Eyes closed tight, she lifted her face to the mirror. Breathing, "One, two, three," she opened her eyes to—magic. Her small breasts spilled out of the low-cut lace, forming actual cleavage. Nipples taut against transparent cups, her fuller breasts seemed moments from falling out toward whatever awaited them.

Of their own accord, Sheila's hands reached for the softness, cupped her breasts, and glided over the nipples. A ripple of response ignited low in her belly, then lower still. With clumsy fingers, she stripped off her skirt, pantyhose, and white cotton briefs. Slipping a protective facial tissue inside the crotch of the sheer bikini panties, she pulled them on and looked in the mirror, waiting for the magic again.

But there was none this time. Her hipbones jutted out like a wire hanger, her narrow frame as graceless and sexless as a skeleton. She should have known better. Trying to ignore the wasteland below, she concentrated on her newly endowed bustline, but it was like standing a sculpture on a Popsicle-stick base. Disconsolate, she bent over to retrieve her own panties. The mirror behind reflected her bent backside, and suddenly the magic returned. Bent over, her bottom filled out into a shape that was almost—sexy. She examined the view from the left, from the right, and was sticking her head between her knees for that view when a voice startled her.

"How are you doing?" the saleslady asked from the other side of the door. "Do you need any help?"

"I'm fine." A little woozy, Sheila gave up on the between-the-knees viewpoint. She couldn't wait to try on the teddy.

In all, she bought enough lingerie to dress scandalously daily for two weeks, and had to force herself to stop there. She felt as if she'd spent her entire life in a desert and had just made it to the oasis. Hi-cut bikinis, thongs, underwires, scalloped lace, silks: she needed it all. As the saleslady lovingly folded bras and tucked scraps of panties into tissue and then into fancy shopping bags with handles, Sheila had a moment of terror. How would she get it all home? She was supposed to be at a Christian seminar. Returning with shopping bags would be impossible to explain. And if her mother demanded to know what was inside? Her hand shook as she gave the clerk her personal check.

"Come again soon," the clerk urged. "We have new garments arriving all the time."

Sheila managed a strangled "Thank you," and veered away, bags in hand. Logic told her to turn right around and return the whole lot, but she could no more imagine giving up those fine things than she could imagine her mother in the throes of an orgasm.

Scents from the food court reminded her that she had missed the bag lunch at the seminar. She juggled parcels and food and sat down to a baked potato, but then couldn't eat. On top of skipping the seminar, she'd lied to church friends, bought a sinful number of sinful underclothes, and now was going to have to return them or throw them away. This day had turned into a disaster. How had she come to this? It occurred to her that if ever prayer was called for, it was now—but no words came. Was this how complete backsliding began?

"Sheila?"

Sheila dropped her fork and looked up. That Yankee, Joan, the one handling the cookbook for the festival, stood above her with a tray.

"May I join you?" Not waiting for an answer, Joan set her tray on the small table and sat down. "I see you've hit the sales. Did you leave anything for the rest of us?"

Mute, Sheila lifted her shoulders in a shrug, trying to soften it with a smile.

Joan lost hers. "Is something wrong?"

Sheila couldn't think how to begin to explain what was wrong. She attempted another smile—perhaps she'd used the wrong facial muscles the first time. "No."

Not looking convinced, Joan unwrapped her fork and stuck it in what looked like broccoli and bits of chicken in thin brown gravy over rice. Sheila had never seen such a combination before. Her mother never served broccoli. Or gravy. A combination like the one on the Yankee's plate looked suspiciously foreign, and Miss Eva didn't truck with such.

Finally regaining her powers of speech, Sheila said, "Do you shop here often?"

"No, my gynecologist is nearby, and after that yearly ordeal I always treat myself to a day of shopping and bad Chinese food." Joan waved her fork at the plate. "I make better chicken and broccoli, but I just can't resist."

"You haven't bought anything." Sheila was wondering if she dared to ask if she could smuggle her unmentionables home in Joan's car. Being from Up North, she probably was used to sinning and sneaking around.

"Actually, I did, but it's a baby gift for someone in Michigan, so I'm having it shipped."

Shipped? You could have purchases shipped? Sheila sensed salvation. What had felt like a tight band constricting her chest finally relaxed. In fact, if she could have everything shipped to her office, maybe she'd go back to the store and look at camisoles and slips.

Cautiously, she took a tiny bite of potato. Yes, she could swallow again. Half listening to the Yankee's idle conversation, Sheila imagined wearing a wispy, satiny bra under a sweater. She mentally added the gel pads. Yes, things were definitely perking up.

Watch Out

By Betty Wilson Beamguard

Exploring a rain forest topped my bucket list, so I decided to visit El Yunque National Forest in Puerto Rico. My husband had no desire to join me, but told me to go right ahead if I had my little heart set on it. I arranged to meet his cousin Jennifer in San Juan where we planned to pick up a car and tour the island. Despite Puerto Rico being as safe as the United States, warnings poured in once I announced my plans.

My mom grew increasingly apprehensive as the time drew near. "Don't get into anything you can't get out of."

Puzzled, I asked for an example.

"Like don't get out on the rough water when it's stormy and watch out for those Haitians." Although I hadn't heard of any showing up in Puerto Rico, I promised to steer clear of stray Haitians who were, at that time, fleeing their homeland.

I had an even stranger conversation with my 93-year-old mother-in-law.

"Are you going by yourself?"

"No, Jennifer's going—Aunt Bonnie's daughter."

"Does she live down there?"

"No, she's flying from Chicago."

"I don't know what you want to go to China for, anyway. I got no desire to go to China myself. Never have."

At that point, I changed the subject.

I knew better than to tell my mother we'd be kayaking, but thought it would be OK to share with my sister. Wrong. She cautioned me not to flip my kayak and get stuck upside down and drown. I explained that it would be an open one, not the Eskimo kind.

My brother-in-law informed me that a couple of his friends had loaded their suitcases into a San Juan taxi with instructions for delivery to their cruise ship. They never saw their luggage again.

I related these warnings to my well-traveled cousin Harriette, thinking she'd join me in laughing at their absurdity. Her response: "Things do take a different spin with women when no male presence is around. If possible, travel with only one bag. It'll be easier to watch. Do watch for pickpockets, usually a bunch of kids who can turn nasty and attack you or people who bump into you in a crowd of tourists."

Harriette went on to relate her experiences in Italy with Gypsy children and pass along tips for intimidating pint-size thieves. Then she warned me to watch out for men wanting to take us on guided tours and advised me not to open my door, even for someone claiming to be hotel management.

Aunt Alice cautioned me about the undertow. Her son, while standing in the waters off San Juan, got carried off by the current. When he waved for help, his wife and her sister smiled, waved back, and went on chatting. Over the next half hour, he fought his way to shore and collapsed at their feet. Only then did they realize he'd been in trouble.

Two days before I left, my husband and I were enjoying breakfast when he said, "Why do you want to spend three days hiking in a rain forest? You might get eaten by one of those big snakes." It took all the self-restraint I could muster to keep from banging my head on the table.

Despite the dire warnings, I managed to survive and enjoy a week of hiking and wandering city streets. I paddled a kayak and swam in a bioluminescent bay off Vieques after dark. However, the trip did not satisfy my desire to hike rain forests. Instead, it merely whetted my appetite.

Riding Double
By Millard R. Howington

The old black mare, Maude,
tolerated me and my little brother
riding her bareback on the hardpan
country road in Georgia, until I tried
to urge her into a trot. Then she
began this gentle swaying back
and forth nothing drastic but just
enough to eventually launch us
into the hot summer air, in tandem,
brother to brother, with me landing
first on my chin, rocks and red dust
spraddling out, and I wondered right
then if this was payback for all of us
watching her mate with that Shetland
Pony (Prince), who was so short he
had to approach her from the top of
a bank behind the chicken houses,
with a slew of cousins attending.

Sailing Yarn
By Robin Lewis

All the great sailing yarns
have already been written.
Melville saw to that,
looking east to Greylock.
Saw, with eyes
of the earliest explorers,
an ocean so close
the mist hush and salt brine
teased from his window pane.
saw whales rising from depths,
islands of trees marooned,
whirling waves of questions
insurmountable even in the
ship of his mind.
Who am I then
to notice fall leaf ships,
their papery hulls clicking
their tiny masts erect, trembling?
Black asphalt puddle—
yesterday's winter rain—
harbor against these wicked winds.

Miz Audrey Goes to Church
By Valerie Keiser Norris

Miz Audrey Baines drove her 1984 Chevy Impala to church on Sunday. Well, a *course* she drove—would it ever occur to any one of those feeble-brained fools she'd raised to drive their poor widowed mother to church? *No*. Too busy with their own foolish lives to worry about the woman who'd spent the best years of hers wiping their fannies, their noses, and anything else that ran dirty. It was the trial of Miz Audrey's life that her own children were so selfish and mean-hearted. She knew she'd raised them better than that!

Miz Audrey eased the car into a handicapped space. She didn't have a sticker, but a woman who felt as poorly as Miz Audrey did should be allowed to park there, which she planned to advise a policeman of should he ever question her. No one ever used the spot, anyway. The Gilfreds always parked in the other handicapped spot, not that Miz Audrey thought Winnie Gilfred was doing himself any favors. That stroke probably meant he should have been exercising all along, so he ought to start now by walking from a farther spot instead of babying himself.

She'd skipped Sunday school that day. Had quit going, truth be told. Since they'd stopped studying God's Word directly from the Bible and started on those preachy books—*Righteous or Rigid; Are You Following the Call or Ready to Fall?; Forward and Backslider*—she'd decided they'd all gone crazy. Did they honestly think the Good Lord wanted them to sit around discussing questions like, "Have you ever been angry at God? Explain." God would probably rather listen to perverts confess their sins between 9:45 and 10:45 each Sunday than listen to that mess!

She took the stairs even though it hurt her knees. The wheelchair ramp wound back and forth across the entire side of the church, adding about a mile of sidewalk to the trip and a good deal of annoyance to Miz Audrey's Sunday mood. Her personal opinion on wheelchair ramps was that by the time you needed one you ought not be expected to go to church anymore. Just sit at home with the television and be waited on. Not that any of *hers* would bestir themselves to wait on her, although Miz Audrey had kept her mother-in-law years after anyone else would have put her in a home. And all that uproar about her will was plain spite; her sisters-in-law had never once offered to take old Miz Baines for more than an afternoon now and then, so why did they think the woman would leave her pitiful little bit of money to any of them? And no matter what they said, old Miz Baines *was* right in the head when she signed that will. She only started slipping just after.

At the door stood the morning's greeters, the Pruters. Fine pair they were. Miz Audrey was certain it was him spied her peeking in the parsonage windows shortly after the new preacher and his la-di-la wife moved in. If anyone had bothered to ask her, she would have explained she was just checking because she thought she'd seen smoke, like a good citizen. What else could she possibly want to look at in the preacher's house? They'd all had a big time teasing her about it and then she was so mad she didn't even try to explain. And that Louella Pruter, acting sweet as pound cake, and the minute you turned your back telling everyone you took graveyard flowers and put them on your own dining-room table. *And so what if I did?* Miz Audrey thought. *What good were they doing rotting away on a grave?* After service, she might stroll back there and check the supply, if her hips didn't hurt too bad.

Quickly she took her seat—third row, center aisle, in an otherwise empty row. Still early, but Miz Audrey had no use for the gabbing going on at the Sunday-school entrance and front door. Bunch of old busybodies. Probably talking about Miz Audrey's youngest, Loveann, arrested on a DUI again. Miz Audrey decided to ignore those gossips and get a head start on reading the bulletin.

Halfway through the list of upcoming events, she let loose with a ladylike snort. The youth group was going to an amusement park, the seniors heading off for the zoo, a two-week day camp was scheduled for children—what, so they could learn to make lanyards and yarn-wrapped eye-of-Gods and other useless junk? Sounded like a country club, not a church! Activities for every age group, just go, go, go, and not a prayer meeting in sight! What on Earth was happening to the church? She had a good mind to stop the preacher after service and let him know just what she thought about all the "Upcoming Activities."

"Good morning!" the new preacher called out, wearing a suit but no robe. If she lived to be a hundred, she'd never get used to that. "Welcome! Isn't this the most glorious morning you've ever seen? What a beautiful Sabbath! Let me call your attention to a few things in the bulletin." And he went on to point out the zoo trip, the amusement park trip, the day camp, and the rest.

Miz Audrey just stared, daring him to look at her. It really wasn't his fault, though, she relented. He was young. He probably had gotten confused. The seminary did that to the young fellows. She just ought to treat him like one of her own, help him see the error of his ways. That convinced her; she'd just point out his confusion to him after church. It was her Christian duty, after all. How else was a young preacher to learn?

She settled in for the service, but she had no more than opened the hymnal to be ready for the first hymn when they were asked to stand and greet those around them. As if everyone hadn't spent fifteen minutes yacking and busy-bodying around already! Well, she'd just sit right there and wait for everyone to sit down like Christians. Humph. It was just like all of them to ignore her like that. Not a one extending the hand of Christian friendship to her. Bunch of hypocrites.

All through the service she made mental notes of her concerns. It was her duty to let the preacher know what people thought about the changes he'd made since he'd arrived. Not that she wanted Rev. Rosewater back. Why, that man hadn't visited her but once the last time she was in the hospital. And had stayed only a few minutes, when Miz Audrey had made it clear that she had a few things to say about the Easter sunrise service he'd held on a mountaintop nearby, instead of on the church grounds. "Miz Audrey, have you ever *attended* a sunrise service?" As if that even mattered. A person was entitled to speak her mind, wasn't she?

The sermon—and it was a sermon even if they called it "The Message" in the bulletin—was about forgiveness. Again. What *were* they teaching in seminary these days? She felt a strong call from the Lord to set the preacher straight before he had the whole town thinking God was some namby-pamby, willing to let bygones be bygones.

The minute the service ended, Miz Audrey bustled toward the door, vying to be one of the first in line. She wasn't, though, and with resignation got in line behind the Pruters. Louella was saying to the person in front of her, "Did you hear about the oldest Winstead boy? Slipped in the church kitchen and dislocated his knee!"

"Oh, no!" the other woman said. "How bad?"

"Bad," Louella said. "It wouldn't go back into place, so the doctor put him in a brace for six weeks, and then he still might have to have surgery."

As the women exclaimed over it as if it were a tragedy, Miz Audrey thought, *Dislocated knee! Why, he ought to try bleeding hemorrhoids! Like shards of glass, like metal trimmings, like* knife blades *when you try to do your business. And that's the trouble! You can't do your business! Sit there and sit there, like a gun loaded but with the trigger broken. And after all that pain, all that agony, sitting on the toilet until you raised a red ring around your backside, just little marbles, no, more like BBs. Not even enough to make a cat scratch. Give me a dislocated knee any day! The boy ought to be ashamed of himself for even mentioning such a thing.*

But of course, being a lady, she couldn't come out and say any of this. You just had to suffer in silence with something like hemorrhoids. Hurt to stand up, hurt to sit down, burning like fire for hours after you go, making you painfully aware of an area you ought not even have to think about; no, there was nothing like it. Why, having six children never hurt so bad! And two of them over nine pounds!

By the time she got her turn with the preacher, he was already looking at his watch. "Good morning, Miz Audrey! Good to see you today! Do you have any plans for this beautiful afternoon? Have you planted your flowers out by the mailbox yet? I sure do enjoy seeing those morning glories when I drive by your house. Now you have a great afternoon." And before Miz Audrey could open her mouth, he was turning to the next person, already talking.

Miz Audrey stood there a moment, trying to get her bearings. Then like a John Deere, she plowed through the blathering crowd and confronted the preacher's wife, who was wearing yet another Sunday dress and just a bit too much eye makeup for the wife of a man of the cloth.

"Good morning, Miz Audrey," the preacher's wife said. "Looks like a fine day, doesn't it? Have you planted your flowers yet?"

What was with these people? Seems like they could ask a person how she was doing.

Miz Audrey started in. "The church doesn't do right by the widda women. I could have lost my house during the flooding but did anyone call? No! It's not like before. The church used to take care of folks. When I was a girl—"

But someone had accidentally knocked down the preacher's little girl, who was howling for her mother.

Miz Audrey looked around one last time—even the church secretary would do. But no, she was signing up volunteers for the blood drive. Miz Audrey gave up. She'd just phone the preacher Monday morning, get him off to a good start for the week.

She looked around for her children, but of course none of them had hauled themselves out to church this morning. It just amazed her; she'd carried those children to Sunday school and church all their lives, and now you couldn't force a one of them to church. It didn't seem to have done any good at all, dragging them to church all those years. She couldn't imagine not going to church, just tempting the devil like that. Evil was everywhere; Miz Audrey didn't intend to let it get a hold on her. And while she still had breath, she didn't intend to let it win over her children, either. She'd just start with the oldest and work her way down. By the time she got to Loveann, she ought to have a pretty good head of steam built up, make an impression on *that* one she'd not soon forget, her with her Saturday nights at the bar and her Sunday mornings God only knew where. Her children weren't doing right by their poor mother. Miz Audrey felt it her motherly duty—her *Christian* duty—to point it out. The Bible says if you see your brother sinning, you should take him aside and point out the error of his ways. She was sure that included children.

As she headed for her Impala, she remembered the flowers. There was absolutely no sense to letting good flowers rot with no one to appreciate them. It was almost a sin, wasn't it? Miz Audrey headed for the graveyard, feeling uplifted. Church always made her feel good.

Fault Line Sonnet #5
By Michael Hugh Lythgoe

Words—human prayers—trip & fall in default.
Our tongues get tied with language in the mind.
Silence is sanctuary from assault.
A faith needs silence for prayers to refine.
Yet, words nudge like animals seek pets;
Or, catch fire like the driest tinder smokes.
Words can echo as the conch shell can let
The sea's breakers play in the ear, waves float
Climbers died on K2 with panache.
Is unprepared the right word? Whose fault?
How incompetent is an avalanche?
A Buddhist in Tibet balances basalt
Stones on peaks, as silent mountains can;
A glacier melting is silent reprimand.

The Shoebox
By S. Jane Gari

There are many places that made me. I'm taking inventory. Gathering all the fragments together and making canvas out of mosaic. Next week I'm getting married, and I need to feel like just one person.

Packing is an act I perform in solitude. My fiancé has offered his help. But I don't want it. His only big move was to college. And his parents are still together. Moving can be cathartic for me in a way I'm glad he'll never understand.

Each piece of memorabilia imposes its voice as it is neatly wrapped, tucked in a box, sealed with tape. A large white shoebox collects odds and ends that deserve more than "Miscellaneous." There is a list on the side of that precious box: address book, diplomas, passport, old letters, photographs.

The box has traveled with me to five states. I always look through it when I'm moving. A ritual. The photo on the top of the stack shows my six-year-old sister and an eight-year-old me in identical winter coats, our eyes red with tears. We are leaving our father's house to return to our mother's. When I was a kid, I thought it was strange for him to photograph us looking so miserable. Now I think he did it to remind himself that we missed him.

When my parents split, we were living in Monroe Falls, Ohio, during the abysmal economy of the early 1980s. Dad had been sleeping on the couch in our den for days. My sister Terri and I had taken refuge under my bed while we listened to our parents shouting at each other in their bedroom. "Divorce" was in

my vocabulary, but it wasn't in my world. It was not yet the epidemic that would later sweep more than half of my friends' lives. It was a remote idea that floated in the same murky realm of sexual innuendo we laughed at without understanding. But it was closing in on us, imposing itself until it was tangible.

It was my father looking up at me, suitcases in hand, while I stood moping at the top of the stairs. It was my mother, sitting us down on the living-room couch we associated with Christmas, Easter, and extended family to present us with a picture she had drawn in crayon. On the far left of the picture was my father, then my mother, me, and Terri. Mom ripped the far-left figure from the page, leaving the three of us alone, save for my father's cartoon thumb that nearly grasped my mother's open hand.

My sister was only five and the vision of our family literally torn asunder sent her reeling to the floor in hysterics. My mother calmly stated that Daddy doesn't live with us anymore, that we would still see him on weekends. She continued talking in that eerie calm, perhaps trying to diffuse my sister's anguish as she writhed on the floor. My mother's voice grew dimmer and was muted by a pounding rhythm in the back of my head that would become the migraines I would know for the rest of my life. For now it was just pain. Unbelievable pain.

In the next few weeks, my mother often voiced her fears that we were just one step away from "the poor house," and although I was not familiar with the exact Dickensian images she intended to conjure, I knew that it wasn't a condition I wanted to endure. I fantasized about being able to get a job so I could assuage her fears, but at seven, I had no skills, no mode of transportation. My mother began dressing in skirts and blouses and painting her nails as her hands rested on the steering wheel of our silver Buick. Interviews. Many interviews.

On yet another fruitless job-search day for my mother, the bus dropped Terri and me off at the bottom of the steep hill that led to our house that modestly sprouted amid others on the cul-de-sac of Forest Hill Drive. As we made our way to the sidewalk, I saw my mom. She was hunched over at the stop sign combing through the grass with her right hand until she found something, plucked it from the ground, and transferred it to her left hand. Then she began combing again. She was sobbing.

We approached my mother cautiously. "What are you doing?" I asked softly.

"I'm looking for money. I saw you throw your lunch down the sewer yesterday."

It was true. She had made me baloney sandwiches every day for three weeks, and I couldn't stand the sight of baloney anymore. The hawk-eyed lunch ladies would report such wastefulness, so I had stashed the wrapped sandwich in my jacket and chucked it down the sewer drain halfway up the hill to my house, stealthily. Or so I thought.

"I'm sorry Mommy. I just couldn't eat it, and I knew you'd be mad."

"Mad!" she shrieked. "Mad! I don't know where our next meal is coming from! I don't know what we're going to

do! I am picking up spare change from the side of the road! This is what I did today while you were in school and while your father was doing God knows what! And you think you can throw a sandwich away! We are headed for the poor house!"

There was that ominous and mysterious threat again. My stomach tightened; I hugged my jacket closer, concealing the second baloney sandwich I knew I couldn't throw away now.

She turned from us and trudged up the hill, counting the change in her left hand. "Seventy-five cents!" she screamed, presumably at us, although her back was turned, and she pumped her fist full of change in mock victory toward the grey sky.

That night, my mother made us peanut butter and jelly for dinner, saying that's all there was. My sister later complained to me while we took our bath that her stomach was growling.

"I have a baloney sandwich I could split with you," I said.

"I don't want baloney."

"Neither do I."

"What's the poor house?" she asked, brushing the hair of her mermaid doll.

"I'm not sure," I responded, disappointed that I couldn't answer her.

Two hours later, I sat up in my bed with the baloney sandwich I had pulled from my jacket. I ate it, each bite soggy with warm mayonnaise. The light from my mother's bedroom seeped under the crack of my door and expanded outward on my floor until it lost itself in the corner among my toys. My mother cried audibly in her bedroom for several minutes before going silent. Her light went out. Change jingled softly, like little bells.

The Saturday after the stop-sign incident, my mother decided to indulge in a luxury: bacon. My sister and I salivated over the aroma from the oven as we watched our cartoons in the adjacent den. And then we smelled smoke. And then we heard the pounding footsteps in the kitchen, the frantic opening of the oven door, and the screams of my mother being burned by bacon grease siphoning off the corner of a tilted baking sheet.

We scurried into the room where my mother, slumped in a corner, oven mitts still in hand, stared at the ceiling, wailing, "I just wanted to make a nice breakfast! I just wanted to make a nice breakfast!"

The wailing tapered off to a whimper while I inspected her arms. She had burned herself, but I couldn't be sure how badly.

"Mom? Are you OK?"

She couldn't answer my question. She only stared at the ceiling and cried, repeating her earlier mantra as if that would somehow resurrect the bacon. Terri sat on a kitchen chair, her legs dangling, her face blank. I called the only other person I could trust and who could help us, the last person my mother probably wanted to see.

I don't know how long it took for my father to get to our house. In my mind, it's as if I told him what happened and then he materialized in our kitchen. But he knelt on the floor, rocking our crying mother gently in his arms, whispering to her, examining her forearm and then holding an ice pack to it. She calmed down after a few minutes, but my father stayed with her, cradling her exhausted body that he folded into his own. Their embrace conveyed all the devastation of La Pieta, and I held that picture in my head for days.

- - -

There are more beautifully hewn pieces that come together now to paint the landscape of my present tense. For these I am grateful, and they will absorb the vast majority of my focus and energy. A wedding. A new life.

I forge myself through the fires of memory burning in boxes, stored away until I sift through the collective symbols of my life, revising them like a manuscript. I'm thankful for the process; it has made finding love possible, but it does not obliterate the past.

I will always have boxes whose seals open periodically like small mouths. They cannot be silenced. Not by my father. Not by my husband. Not by anyone.

Why the Snake Died
By Betty Wilson Beamguard

In the hall, I come upon a snake
the size of a pencil, gray and black.
I summon my husband.
Rattlesnake, he says.
Are you sure? It's just a baby.
Can't take a chance.
Get me something to kill it with.

I bring his walking stick,
a gift from his retirement party;
watch him jab repeatedly,
fight tears as the little fellow thrashes,
struggles for life, then stills,
his head smashed flat.

I carry him to the porch,
open his mouth, find no fangs,
refer to our field guide—rat snake,
harmless, helpful in controlling rodents.

The diamond pattern that was to
camouflage him during his first year
caused him to be identified as a threat.

I draw parallels to war;
violence spawned by fear;
misidentification of the enemy.

Smoke
By Maureen Sherbondy

"Raise five," says Bill, the bail bondsman/bodyguard sitting beside Teresa at the oval table.

Teresa hesitates, wonders if he's bluffing, studies his red-suited eight, nine, ten, and king. She tosses five chips into the pot, then peeks at her own down cards again. Ace, king, ace. Yesterday, her first day in the poker room, she wasn't discreet enough; she caught the loser next to her looking at her hand. At least there's no smoke in this room. There's enough of that in the casinos and outside.

It takes every bit of control not to smile at the ace, king, ten, and four showing. Her goal is to keep from giving away her hand. It's hard to stifle a smile when she has a flush or a straight, even three of a kind.

For hours, she's been making tough decisions: when to go out, when to stay in, when to bluff, when to raise. Glancing at her plastic rack of chips, organized in neat rows of 20, she realizes that she is down only four chips, and if she wins this pot, she'll be up by about 50.

Teresa feels very brave, playing at the seven-card-stud table with the others. It's sort of like the World Series Poker Tournament she'd seen on television recently, only this is just a game, not a tournament. Even though it's the low-minimum one-dollar/five-dollar table, it is a few steps up from her monthly poker game with the girls.

The guy next to her, Bill something, the guy with many jobs, seems friendly. He's been talking to everyone for the last two hours, but mostly to her. He asks where she's from and what she likes to do. He smiles at her whenever she raises him. In Richmond, she wouldn't normally socialize with a total stranger, especially one who probably carries a gun. Her heart pounds in her chest. Something about the guy excites her. He has a cocky but adorable grin. Bill lifts his beer glass, empties it in one swig, beer drips over his full lips. He wipes it away with his large, tan hand. He reminds her of someone she once knew. She twirls a long strand of hair, trying to conjure up who he looks like.

When she was single, she met lots of guys, flirted every weekend at bars and dance clubs. But for some reason, she can't remember how to flirt. Did she smile, look at them, then look away? Why can't she remember? It's as if seven years of marriage has erased that part of her memory, banished it to the desert.

A cocktail waitress, all legs and short skirt, arrives as if psychic, and replaces his empty glass. Bill tosses two chips on her dark tray while keeping his eyes on the growing pot.

Bill is telling her all about the criminals he catches in LA, informs her that the relatives who put up the bond with their house, or savings, usually let him know where the criminals are hiding. Teresa rolls her eyes at the information. He flashes his bulky silver watch in front of her face, proudly announcing, "Legal Time, for when I take them in."

Loud off-key melodies belt out from the next room. Women singing at the top of their lungs, "Bye Bye Miss American Pie," "Girls Just Wanna Have Fun," and "We Are the Champions." She recognizes the tunes, but the words are all wrong. Teresa tries to focus on the folks at her own table.

She finds Bill's conversation more interesting than Irving from Jersey City, or Ruth from Detroit, who keeps asking for poker advice and distracting Teresa from her own hand. Teresa raises one last time, then proudly announces, "full house," as the others flip their cards down in defeat.

She gathers her purse and her rack of chips, smiles and says goodbye to the table. Bill places his warm hand over hers. His words beginning to slur, he says, "Don't leave." She pulls her hand away quickly as a strange vibe runs through her body. Feeling her cheeks blush, she leaves the poker room.

In the casino, she is flooded by the loud trio of sloshed 20-something-year-old women, sitting at the boring wheel. They are going through a whole medley of pop tunes from the early 1990s, belting out songs. It's too much for Teresa; she can't stay here another minute.

She can't find her friend, Libby, who promised she'd meet her at 1 a.m. Just as well, she supposes, they aren't getting along this time, anyway. Last year's trip went smoothly. But this time, Libby is upset about being dumped by her fiancé, and losing her job, and has been taking it out on Teresa. She's been snappy and bossy, moody. This morning, Libby yelled at Teresa for getting up at 7 instead of 8 a.m. What could she do? Leave? Get a different room?

Away from the singing women, Teresa makes it to the conveyor belt walkway that leads her outside. She chokes on the fire-scent in the air. The California fires have blown smoke into the area and her eyes now hurt. She hopes it won't affect the flight home tomorrow. On the street, three short Hispanic men snap cheap brochures against her hands. Trying to ignore the naked men and women on the covers, she pushes her hands into her pockets, looks away from the men. She nearly bumps into a very tall transvestite, wearing a skimpy tiger-striped dress and too much eye makeup. The man is so tall he towers over her like a giraffe in this Las Vegas jungle. He flicks a long pierced tongue at her. She turns toward the dirty sidewalk.

She crosses the lit-up street, amazed at all the people walking around after 1 a.m. She's not sure if she should stay up and play some table games or hit the sack early. The tall buildings and colorful, red, blue, green flashing neon signs still amaze her, as do the restaurants and casinos open all night. How does anyone sleep here?

The Brooklyn Bridge, the New York Skyline, the Italian-themed Venetian with elaborate columns, the Eiffel Tower, all thrown together in one street, a bizarre montage of places that don't belong together. This fake world plunked down in the middle of a desert.

She'll need a vacation from this trip. She is not used to keeping such late hours. Crossing the street, she notices a young couple pushing a stroller. The baby is asleep, oblivious to the lights and smoke-haze around her. When she returns home, James expects her to begin a family. He told her it's time; he is 29, he is ready to be a daddy now.

Something suddenly tugs at Teresa, both a warm maternal feeling and a scary, queasy feeling. She wants and doesn't want a baby. She doesn't feel ready yet to be a mom. She likes the neat order of her life, working from eight to five, getting nine straight hours of sleep a night. She enjoys her morning jog, and the slow Sundays, waking up late, lounging around, reading the thick *New York Times* until three in the afternoon.

She loves coming to Vegas, the thrill of the cards, the probability of getting certain hands in poker. The gamble, trying to beat the odds. If she has a baby, when will she get to come here again? When will she get to do what she wants to do?

Not yet sleepy, Teresa sits down at a *Let it Ride* table. Only one other person, a boring one, is playing. She has two classifications: the dull ones who play and have no interest in talking, and the animated ones who share their life story in three hands. The animated ones make playing interesting, even if she is losing—at least she gets free stories for the price of a hand. Yesterday, a friendly one, who was a little shaken, told her about the fireball that just missed his car on the way here. He just made it through before the freeway was blocked off.

After three bad hands in a row, she says, "Give me some good cards."

A familiar voice sneaks up from behind, "There you are." Bill plops his large body down. She hadn't noticed he was six-four when they were at the low poker table. His bond escapees probably take one look at him and offer up their hands to the cuffs without protest.

"Why'd you leave the Mirage?" he asks, spitting beads of beer into her face.

"Huh. Oh, just wanted to quit while I was ahead," she answers.

"Flock of Seagulls is playing. You like them?" Bill raises his long face, as if trying to find the speakers.

"Yeah, I used to. Nineteen-Eighties?" She says unenthusiastically as possible, even though she loves the song. Now it clicks, the Eighties—Bill reminds her of Carl, a boyfriend she dated for three months years ago. Like Bill, Carl knew how to have a good time. He was impulsive and inconsistent, but excitement swirled around him like mosquitoes near flesh. Girls and trouble followed him everywhere.

Has he followed her? How does he know she left and came here? She suddenly sees him as a fireball coming at her, and she doesn't know where to go. It's exciting and scary at the same time. She feels his breath on her face, hot as fire.

Leaning in, he says, "Yeah, Eighties. Hey you know, I'm also a bodyguard."

"You told me," she says, staring at her cards.

"Want me to be *your* bodyguard?"

Her wedding band catches the light. She thinks of the slogan "Everything that happens in Vegas stays in Vegas." Is she really thinking this? Could she really mess around and leave it here? She tries to focus on her pair of fives, sets her cards under her chips.

"Put it over *here!*" The dealer scolds her.

His tag says *Arvis, New Mexico*. Arvis seems grumpy. Maybe he doesn't like this late shift, maybe he misses New Mexico. Teresa glares at Arvis.

"Hey, chill out, Arvis. Ease up on the lady." Bill winks at Teresa.

Teresa smiles.

"Yeah, like I'm Clint Eastwood's bodyguard next week. Me and Clint go to parties, hang out. I keep my eye on things, you know, *things*."

Arvis pushes chips towards Teresa. She piles them into a neat stack, on top of the other five-dollar chips, as if trying to gain control over this night through neatness. Bill is so different from James. Bill smiles a lot, James is so serious. Bill seems fun; she misses having fun, excitement. Keeping a house, paying bills, planning a family is so serious. So adult.

Between the smoke and the cards coming her way, she looks to the right and sees Bill sipping his beer. He is watching her. She can't remember the last time her own husband looked at her like Bill is looking at her right now. He wants her. He isn't even playing at this table. She tries to spot his gun. He wears jeans and an un-tucked black shirt. Where could he hide a gun? She wonders what a gun would feel like in her own hands. She wonders what his body looks like under that shirt.

A wall is crumbling inside her, the firm wall of marriage that keeps men away. Her husband isn't here, and she doesn't even miss him. *Where the hell is Libby?* A voice screams in her head. She checks left to right, beyond the blackjack tables and the roulette wheels, towards the entrance. It's too cold. Cool fire-smoke air seeps through the open doors. The loud shriek of a shocked female winning at slots rises in the background. Heavy silver dollars clank against a metal bin. Everything seems fuzzy with cigar and cigarette smoke. She quickly picks up her neat pile of chips and leaves the casino, walking as fast as she can.

Libby would keep her out of trouble. Libby would be the voice of reason. She'd say something like, "Hit the road, Mr. Bill!"

What should she do? She makes a list of choices in her head, just like she and James do when they are trying to make important decisions. One, call security and have them walk her to the room; two, find Libby; three, try to lose Bill, then go up to the room.

Even if she makes it to her room, she'll be afraid to stay there alone. What if he follows her and wants to come in? Will she want to keep him out? Number two is the only option. With each step, she wonders what has she done to deserve this. Finally, at the entrance to the Mirage, she looks over her shoulder and doesn't see him. Her heart slows down. She wipes the sweat from her palms into her jeans.

Pausing in front of the tiger's glass partition, she cranes her neck up at the TV overhead. It's the image of the two tiger trainers, one of whom is supposedly in a hospital recovering from an awful tiger attack. Today she passed a shrine of flowers and notes from well-wishers placed in front of the hotel. Maybe he is really dead. Nothing seems right here: the fire smoke, the advertisements for this tiger show duo, the big man who is coming on to her. The tiger is inside her head when she closes her eyes. Who is the tiger? Her husband? Bill? Is she really married? Or, is she back to her single days when this kind of thing happened all the time? This could be a first date.

Someone taps her shoulder, she jumps, her eyes spring open to see Bill just inches away.

"Found you," says Bill with a huge smile. He pushes a strand of blonde hair from her shivering mouth. His eyes are blue like James's, but warm blue, not cold and distant. He moves his long fingers over her lips, then pulls her face toward his. Her head spins, she chokes on the smoke, or something else that is hanging in the air.

She shakes her head back and forth, slowly. "No, no, I can't. I'm married."
As if the words are a red light that will stop him from moving forward. Reflexively, she pushes her hand into his stomach. She feels his firm muscles. Her hand lingers. "I'm *married!*"

"Really? Where's your husband, then? If he's not here, you're single, right?"

"He let me come here. I come here every year."

"He let you? If you were my wife, I'd be here with you. I wouldn't let you be away from me for a minute."

She is so tired and confused. She wants to close her eyes and be back at her safe home in Virginia, but she wants to kiss this exciting man next to her and never go back home again.

She thinks of the road to LA—closed. The haze of fire is stuck in the air, obscuring clarity. Her hotel room seems countries away. She wonders if the tiger trainer is dead or alive. She wonders who would know the truth between life and death in this place of facades and neon signs.

She lets him kiss her. She kisses him back, then pushes him away.

"No, I can't do this. I can't."

Tears cover her warm mouth. When she turns away to run, two cars nearly hit her as she crosses against the red light. Running through the casino, she lunges at the elevator button, tears blurring her vision. With one hand, she presses the 11 button, while the other hand touches her still-warm lips.

Kitesurfer in New South Wales Hit by Tail
By Maureen Sherbondy

The kitesurfer is hit by the whale's tail—
is this how it happens? We are sailing along
then some creature flails around
in the air, bumps us on the head,
hitting us with a literal tail, or perhaps
a literary tale, a fairy tale where
the witch is about to bake the children,
but they escape from the candy house
and run through the woods, or the Prince
is leaning in to kiss Sleeping
Beauty. You get the point.
Pay attention, the universe
wails. Go ahead, drift in
and out of the world, your legs
skimming the ocean's effusive
foamy lips, the wave swallowing
your feet. It could have been worse.
Jonah was swallowed by that same
whale. You, dear kitesurfer,
were merely whacked on the head,
enlightened while at the beach,
a grand tale to tell for decades to come.

Quitting
By Kim Catanzarite

She would not have a cigarette. The blue box wedged in between a flask and tumbler would remain in the cabinet above the sink. Safe and sound and exactly where it should be. She would not touch it—or even check to make sure it was there. If need be, she would suck on the puffer the doctor prescribed. The little white plastic thingy with the nugget of nicotine inside soothed her nerves to some extent, hence the reason it sat on the table in front of her now, beside the mug of black coffee.

She hated Saturday mornings. Especially after Friday nights like the Friday night she just had. If someone in her past had told her she'd be having Friday nights like the one she had last night at her age (nearly twice that of some of the company she'd been keeping of late), she would have laughed in their face. It would have been a nervous laugh, mind you, because she always worried she would end up alone. And here she was, in her fourth decade, living with just her dog in an apartment—and her mother a few blocks away, on the telephone several times a day.

Eric was a shit. He knew her whole life depended on whether he called. After what she did to him, she doubted he would. Too many rum and cokes didn't wear well on her. Not on an empty stomach. Not with him ignoring her the way he did. But she hadn't smoked—that was the good thing. She'd been too drunk to fit the dollars into the machine's skinny slot and none of Eric's little friends would give one up after all the bragging she did about quitting for two months.

How did she end up with guys like him? Dead end, unmarriageable guys. How did she, as her mother said, "always find them"? Maybe they found her. Had her mother ever thought of that? It wasn't like she enjoyed being dumped. She didn't look forward to the period of mourning that followed or the loneliness that dug its nail in after that.

Last night, she admitted, could have been prevented. No one made her go to The Mill. Eric had a gig, she'd read about it in the paper. He'd stopped telling her where and when weeks ago. But so what? She was sick of staying away so he could "mingle freely" (mingling, he claimed, was key to the band's popularity). Just like she was sick of the groupies she was supposed to pretend didn't exist. All those girls wanting a piece of him. The leader of a crappy cover band! Not that Eric didn't have talent. He did. And charisma, certainly. The charisma made up for what beauty his face and body lacked. But none of that mattered anymore, because surely he would not call her, would not invite her for dinner or drinks or sex at her place anytime soon. Not after what she'd done to him.

But maybe it was better this way. If he didn't call, she wouldn't have the chance to make it up to him, to grovel and sniffle and tell him how much she needed the sporadic pleasure he provided. If he didn't call, perhaps that much more of her dignity would remain intact. Dignity—she hardly remembered what if felt like.

She flicked the puffer and watched it spin. If she could give up a 25-year smoking habit, certainly she could give up Eric. If he didn't call, maybe she would suck it up for once and get on with her life. Avoid the bars. Eat a real meal even if it meant gaining a pound. Go to work without a hangover. The nightlife wasn't meant for 40-something working gals—at least, not the brand of nightlife the girlfriends of lead singers led. Maybe if she avoided the bars and got some decent sleep and woke up with a clear head, she'd see the world in a new light and try to meet someone her own age. A divorcee, maybe, or an ex-con—ha ha—single middle-agers weren't exactly lurking on every corner. *Where do the un-young go to meet a suitable partner?* Her therapist had asked the question (minus the "un-young") over a decade ago, back when she still believed therapy might make a difference. But she didn't have an answer then and wished a plausible one would show itself now.

At least she was thinking about meeting other men. At least she could do that much without breaking down. But maybe the hangover allowed her this luxury. Her brain still numbed by the cold drink and the hot drama she put it through the night before.

Why did Eric have to disappear into the kitchen with that waitress, if all he needed was to settle a bill? Even if his ears were ringing thanks to Cheech's overzealous amp and he couldn't hear a word the girl was saying, he knew her better than that. He knew she would run in there after them.

Maybe he'd send her a text message just to say hi (he sometimes did after a fight), then wait a couple of weeks for things to blow over and show up on her doorstep one unsuspecting night.

Or maybe he wouldn't, and she'd spend the rest of her life alone, with just her dog, and daily calls from her mother.

She lifted the puffer to her lips and sucked deeply. The mix of nicotine and oxygen burned, but the rush that followed felt like a hand on her back, patting down her nerves, consoling her.

At least she hadn't smoked. Then on top of everything else she'd feel guilty about that. During her last visit, the doctor told her she wasn't a kid anymore, that she needed to quit such detrimental behavior. She only hoped she wouldn't get cancer and die alone, with her mother at the other end of the telephone and her dog at her bedside.

She had spent so much of her life feeling lonely, it wasn't fair. Even when she had boyfriends, there were plenty of lonely nights. Thank God she didn't have a cigarette last night, because then she would worry even more about getting cancer and dying alone. She felt the tears coming and decided it would be a good idea to get the emergency pack from the cabinet and destroy it tube by tube. Then she wouldn't be tempted anymore. Plus, it would be symbolic. A symbol of her new cancer-free life. Eric wasn't going to call and that was fine. She was probably better off without him, as the saying goes.

She reached for the package of cigarettes and grabbed a saucer from the cabinet (she'd tossed all the ashtrays weeks ago), then returned to the table. She removed one of the white tubes and crumbled it in her hand, watching the flakes fall like tiny leaves to the plate below. She flicked the lighter and the pile burned with a fizzzzzzzz. It felt good, burning the bad stuff out of her life. And then the phone rang like an alarm. Eric's number a stamp in her eye.

She pulled a butt from the pack and pushed TALK. "Hello?"

"Hey."

Oh Jesus. She balanced the cigarette upon her bottom lip, flicked the lighter, and inhaled.

"Are you smoking?"

"What?" The smoke hovered in the cave of her mouth. "Why do you care?"

He made a spitting sound. "You know what? You have no self-respect. No respect at all, *that's* your problem."

She looked at the cigarette with disdain, pressed its pretty orange head into the saucer. Who the hell was he to tell her she had no respect? Him with his "yo" and his "dude" and his stupid singing voice. He was a decade younger than she, a pretend rock star, a noncommittal. How did she always find them?

"I think I may have a little more than you think." She banged the END button before pitching the phone into a pillow on the couch.

The dog, roused by the phone toss, raised his ears.

She walked to the back of the house and stopped at the entrance to her bedroom. She did not cry. Did not even fume. She merely stood there. And looked. The place resembled a construction site. Clothing piled like garbage around the periphery—the bed, unmade, waiting for someone (surely not a prince) to come. The mirror reflected a veil of cobwebs. One sad painting in the corner clung to the end of a wire. The room was tired. Tired of waiting for life to begin.

It was a dramatic review, perhaps, but true all the same.

She approached the mirror. Tried to see herself as stranger might. Not so bad for a middle-ager, not even after a rough night. Her eyes, though red-rimmed, had a softness to them, a kindness. Her hair, still full, still dark and young, fooled a lot of men into thinking she *was* young. But what was the use?

She would call her mother as she did every day, and tell her nothing was new. Then she would climb into her unmade bed and sleep until her brain cooled and the alcohol exited her body. When she got up, she would clean house. Get rid of everything she didn't need, shake off the cobwebs. Let in some light. Maybe even change her phone number. She could feel it, the optimism fighting its way back in. . . .

If she stopped trying so hard, she was bound to find someone.

Even if it was only herself.

Myrtle Beach Sonnet
By Michael Hugh Lythgoe

I was a long time away, returning
To relearn the ocean's rhythmic lessons.
I find you in darkness, like our first meeting.
Not much moon, but lights on the horizon—
Cruise ship sailing north to some port city.
A container ship pirates might steal in a fight?
To stare from shore is to see eternity.
Over gray distances, high tide drags the night.
Some say renewal is being born again.
My parents saw this ocean near the end
Of their landlocked lives. Only waves survive
The enduring rush ashore, repeatedly falling,
Bearing patterns in the brine, crests spilling.
The sea repeats deep lapses. Some revive.

Declaration of Independence
By Jim McFarlane

"If you put me in a nursing home, I'll remove you from my will."

My widowed mother repeated that every time I visited. It was a plea, an order, a threat, and a fear, all rolled into one.

She lived alone in the house my father built in 1950—three bedrooms, 1,400 square feet, and a three-percent mortgage paid in full. After a mild stroke and a leg brace 10 years ago, my brother hired a woman to come in three mornings a week to cook and freeze meals, run errands, and—most awkward of all—maneuver my mother from her walker onto the bathtub chair for a bath. Other than that, Mom was independent and self-sufficient.

Even after a substantial gift to each of her eight grandchildren for a down payment on a first house, Mom still had plenty of money to live on. Because she never spent any. Well, not exactly. A lunch-time visit to KFC was a treat. But Mom didn't need anything.

More accurately, she didn't want anything.

On an obsolete computer, she played solitaire—a hand-strengthening exercise, she explained—and watched the screen savers displaying photos of grandchildren and great-grandchildren. Her VCR never blinked 12:00 because she religiously recorded her soap operas and *Jeopardy* in case she fell asleep or company came at inappropriate times. If the weather was good, she left the inside walker by the door and cautiously climbed down four steps. With the rusty outside walker, she strolled up and down the driveway and then sat in a sturdy iron chair. Every spring she wanted the gutters cleaned and mildew scrubbed off the oak-shaded front porch. Once she asked for an easier-to-grasp handle to the kitchen door.

She was content.

Last year, Mom had enough pain from a stuck gallstone that my brother took her to the hospital—in her opinion, one short step from a nursing home. Her age, too many medicines, and medical complications all combined to put her in a rapid downward spiral. Her last coherent words were "Take me home."

With Hospice's help, we carried her home from the hospital. The next day, a month shy of her 95th birthday, she died where she belonged—in her home of 58 years.

Today I contemplate retirement. Despite good health, I'm designing a house that my wife and I can live in for the rest of our lives: no stairs to climb, no gutters to clean, and no exterior wood to clean and paint.

How much closet space do we need?

When we cleaned out my mother's house, we gave away most of the furniture and clothes. But I filled the back seat of my car with framed pictures from the walls and several shoeboxes of photographs, faded newspaper clippings, and a few old letters. I never knew my mother was homesick her first weeks of college, barely 17 years old and

30 miles from the home in which she was born.

That reminded me that both my parents graduated from college in 1932 with teaching degrees. Back then, a young person had no grandiose expectations of material comfort. Food every day, a few clean clothes, and a job were lofty goals. Today's newspaper claims this recession is the worst since 1933 and threatens that four-dollar gasoline will return when the economy improves. My mother knew how to survive rough economic times. Maybe she has a few more things to teach me.

Does my retirement house really need 3,000 square feet to heat and cool and keep clean? On the computerized house plan, I erase a couple of spare bedrooms and reduce the size of closets and windows, producing more wall space for family photographs.

My wife looks over my shoulder. "Where's my big hall closet?"

"If we don't buy stuff, then we won't require as much space to store it and our children and grandchildren won't need to throw it away when we die."

"Where will those children and grandchildren sleep when they visit?"

"OK. You can have a third bedroom. But everything will be handicapped-accessible—one story, doorways wide enough for a wheelchair, and the porch on the same level as the house. Now look at this Internet picture of a roll-in shower big enough for a wheelchair."

She frowns. "It looks like something that belongs in a nursing home."

"Which do you prefer—this shower in our house or us in a nursing home?"

Home on the Road
By Steve Heckman

"Hey Andy, look. Ain't that your house?"

That was a good one. I kept my head down, eyes on the remains of my mac and cheese. "April first was last week, Shawn."

"No, man, I'm serious." He was sitting in his usual seat in the far corner of the booth by the window, where he could see back down Liberty Street. "Looks like your place to me."

I took the last bite of my meal, chewed a couple times, swallowed, head still down. "Well you see, Shawn, my 'house,' as you call it, is up by Third and Buffalo, and unless a fire leveled about four city blocks between here and there this morning while I was on a creeper under that Yukon and you were jerkin' off into the glove box of that Caddy while you were supposed to be replacing a window motor, you can't see up there from here."

Alvin, sitting next to Shawn, started snickering.

I could see Tarssha's Reeboks out of the corner of my eye, long dark legs going up out of my field of vision. "Uh, Tarssha, can I get my check? It's getting to be time to get back to work."

The Reeboks didn't move. I glanced up at her. She was looking out the window, eyes kind of big.

I followed her gaze.

A 10-year-old white Ranger short-bed was rolling slowly past the diner window, one of those magnetic yellow flashing lights stuck on the roof. After a few seconds, a faded International cab-over with real wide mirror brackets followed, slow and easy, pulling something.

I put down my fork, willing it not to clatter. Now the front end of a 1978 Fleetwood 12-foot-by-70-foot came slowly into view; a six-foot bow window—an option on that model—on the side where the living room would be; then the entrance door, smudged black around the knob like a mechanic came home to it every night; brand-new tires on the rusty wheels, like the old ones had dry-rotted; then a small frosted window, the kind that would be in a bathroom halfway down a hall; then another larger, master bedroom window with a duct-tape-covered hole the size of a worn-out 12-inch Crescent wrench would make if someone flung it after stripping the top nut on the left rear shock on an '84 F150 because, even though he had $6,000 worth of Huskies in his tool cabinet at, say, some Chevy dealer, he had nothing but crap in the spackling bucket he called a tool box at home; and finally the back of the trailer, chalky white paint mildewed, like the neighbor in back had a big hemlock tree that kept that end in the shade all the time.

My house.

"I guess Mary June had second thoughts." Shawn was still looking back up Liberty Street.

Alvin appeared perplexed. "Second thoughts?"

"Yeah, second thoughts about only takin' everything but the kitchen sink. Looks like she got that, too."

That damned sink. I had just put in a new one, the best stainless-steel model Lowe's had, last month, after listening to Mary June whine about the almond porcelain one for like 20 years. The next day, I came home from work and the TV was gone and her closet was empty and I knew it was over.

Barry and Larry were sitting next to me, talking about the Penguins-Rangers game last night, finishing each other's sentences the way twins do, something about a short-handed goal. The only two hockey fans in the world who had never been outside South Carolina. Larry happened to look out the window and said, "Hey Andy, isn't that your place?"

"Uh, yeah." I was waiting for Shawn to make a crack about Barry and Larry being in their own world, but he was still looking back up the street. His face had changed, like maybe he thought things were going too far. "Now what, Shawn?"

"Uh, you ain't gonna like the chase car, Andy."

Slowly, like the other two vehicles had, the chaser came into view. It was the Mustang convertible, top down, another flashing yellow light stuck on the trunk lid. Except Mary June wasn't at the wheel. Some guy in coveralls was. She was in the back, sitting up on top of the seatback, like she was in a parade. I guess in a way she was. She was wearing the black dress with the spaghetti straps, the dress she bought the same day I put in the new sink, the dress that maxed out our last Visa card. Later, she'd worn it to the hearing. No wonder the judge gave her everything she asked for. Now it looked out of place, but she looked good in it. Too good.

She waved cheerily toward the diner as she passed. She couldn't see inside on such a sunny day, but all of our trucks were parked outside, so she knew we were in there. She always wondered why the five of us drove four trucks three blocks every day for lunch, instead of all piling into one, or walking.

Walking. That was a laugh.

Shawn was craning his neck, watching her 'til she was on out of sight, rolling his tongue around his lips. Shawn always rallied. Alvin was back to chuckling, like he couldn't think of anything else to do. And I had thought at first that he was laughing with me. Barry and Larry were going on about icing-the-puck being waived during overtime or some fuckin' thing.

I felt Tarssha's hand on my shoulder. I looked up at her. She stared at the now-empty window, eyes flashing. "If you want me to, Andy, I'll track her down and kill her."

"That's sweet of you, Tarssha, but I have all these supportive friends. They'll help me get through it all."

She leaned down. "If you need to crash somewhere, we have room. Rodney won't mind."

"Yeah, I'm sure he wouldn't. Sweaty, greasy white guy sprawled on the couch, kids starin' at him. Thanks, T, but I'll be OK."

"OK? What does that mean? Sleepin' in the truck? You just come on over."

"Uh, I'll think about it. Thanks, really."

"I better get those checks. It's five 'til. You don't want to keep The Man waiting."

A couple of minutes later, as we walked out of the diner, I said, "Shawn, tell Bernardi I'll be a little late. I better go get my clothes before it rains. I'll work over if he wants me to."

"Gotcha covered."

I got in the truck, backed out, and drove slowly down Liberty Street to Third, then right two blocks to Buffalo and straight at the stop sign. Third driveway on the left, 312 Third Street.

An empty lot.

I knew it would be empty—it had to be, but it still caught me a little. Nothing in the mailbox. A 12-foot-by-70-foot rectangular brown scar down one lot line.

Mary June had gotten the movers to stack the skirting from around the trailer in a neat pile. The tarp I usually kept over the lawnmower was stretched over a lump in the middle of the yard—my clothes, I knew. I also knew that when I took off the tarp, the clothes would be neatly folded and stacked, not just dumped there. My tool bucket held down one end of the tarp. On the other end, upside down so it would sit flat, was a 22-inch stainless-steel Lowe's sink, plumber's putty still stuck to the bottom of it. I pulled out my phone and snapped a picture of it. Shawn had to see that.

What chance did a man have? Mary June could rub a knot in your neck with one hand and twist the knife at the same time with the other, and mean them both, and enjoy them both, and see or feel no contradiction in any of that.

I was going to miss her.

Sudden Death
By Missy Nicholson

There are two ways to die: suddenly and not. Our family's experienced both kinds of dying. My husband's brother died suddenly in a car crash, but it took my grandmother two decades to die from diabetes and heart disease. And my aunt died within an hour of her esophagus rupturing (although one could argue that alcoholism killed her slowly for 30 years).

My mom's story is different. When we found out she had breast cancer, my stomach immediately began to churn with the acid of the unknown. Would Mom beat the five-year survival rate? Or would she become another statistic in a fight against a despicable disease? Only God knew the answer, and that meant I wasn't in control. I wasn't happy.

After a second mammogram and an ultrasound, it took two weeks to see a surgeon. He was pretty nonchalant about the whole thing. "No big deal . . . let's do a biopsy . . . think we can get it all that way." It took another three weeks to schedule the biopsy. When the surgeon came out to talk to us, he wouldn't meet our eyes. It was bigger than he thought. Lymph nodes had to be removed. He thought he got it all, but he wasn't sure.

Anger I didn't realize I had finally found a target. I was furious with the doctor! How much had the cancer spread during the five weeks we did a "hurry up and wait" routine with the nonchalant surgeon? And then I realized I was mad at Mom. Why hadn't she taken better care of herself? She smoked, was overweight, took hormones, and ate those microwavable meals in the plastic trays. I thought all this, although I'm quite sure, and I really hope, I never said it out loud.

Soon after, Mom and I were in the oncologist's office for her first visit. He introduced himself, and I liked him immediately. He wasn't nonchalant. He was direct. Mom's cancer was dangerous and her treatment would be extensive. He left us to order blood work.

I turned around to tell Mom how much I liked him, and she was just sitting there on the end of the exam table crying.

She looked at me. "I am so sorry. I didn't mean for this to happen. Please forgive me."

So, in that great way mothers know things, she knew I blamed her at least partially for getting breast cancer. And my mother was scared. I could see it in her face, hear it in her voice, feel it in the tremor of her hands as she touched my arm. I would work hard to take care of her, forgive her, and forgive myself.

As this new chapter of our life unfolded, we spent many hours together. She took chemo and radiation and battled nausea and fatigue. We did crossword puzzles, sorted old pictures, and planned camping trips to the beach. We discussed lots of things, but never the elephant sitting right between us. We never discussed the possibility that she might die.

Mom finished treatment and we resumed a normal life. Over a year passed and life was good. But we were always waiting for the phone to ring.

One day, it did.

Mom's counts were elevated. The oncologist asked if she was feeling any pain.

"Well, my stomach's been hurting, but I figure it's just heartburn or something."

It was something. So, Mom began a new cycle of treatment and was in and out of the hospital several times when the chemo killed the good cells right along with the bad. The cancer counts lowered for a time, but they never got down to a level that put a smile on her doctor's face.

The elephant in the room got bigger and bigger, and Mom went through a bitter stage. "Why me?" she would ask. "I'm a pretty good person. There are some bad people in this town—why not them?" I was terrified when Mom voiced these things. I wanted to be the blissfully unaware daughter and her, the in-control mother.

In January 2003, we left the cancer center with mixed feelings. Mom was skipping chemo because her white-blood-cell count was too low. Although tired, she wouldn't have to endure nausea for the next two weeks. She wasn't supposed to spend a lot of time in public places. But Mom wanted to eat lunch out, so we did and I'm glad. When cancer is winning, you take whatever moments you get . . . even at a Chili's Restaurant.

We ate burgers and fries. She was completely bald, and her face was puffy from the meds. The couple at the next table kept staring at her, and my blood began to boil. But when Mom started talking, I listened. Apparently, she wasn't going to ignore the elephant any longer.

She told me death was inevitable, and she decided to accept it with grace and dignity. She didn't want her grandchildren to remember her as the sickly woman they visited quietly in her dark bedroom. She wanted them to have memories of home-baked cookies, summer beach trips and magical Christmases. She wanted the rest of us to remember the way she lived her life—without apology and with a fierce passion for her family. Because of her courage, grace and dignity—because of the way she lived—our memories far exceed her expectations. But in the deep dark corners of many nights, I still remember the way she died.

One Monday in late April 2003, she had returned to the hospital.

The oncologist pulled me aside. "It's time to call in the family."

So when my Dad, brother, aunts, uncles, and friends gathered in Mom's hospital room, I realized how terrifying this must be for her. She looked around the room with wide eyes, trying to keep a smile on her face and a joke on her lips. But she knew we had called in the family. She knew what that meant.

By Friday, Mom was losing control of bodily functions. Trying to be a lady while her room was full of folks was exhausting. Dad was exhausted from staying at the hospital 24/7. I was exhausted because well-meaning family and friends kept asking: "How much time does she have?" "When will Hospice come in?" I wanted to yell, "I'm sorry I called in the family and now Mom's not dying on schedule." Instead, I asked everybody to stay away the next day, and I begged Dad to go home and get some rest.

That last Saturday was a good day. It was just Mom and me. I was selfish in asking everyone else to leave us alone, but I don't regret it. We had the time to act like a mother and daughter one last time. We looked through a catalog together and picked out a birthday present for Dad. We reminisced about 30-plus years spent camping at the beach. We laughed about silly things like the annoying habits of husbands, bragged about her incredibly smart grandkids, and got up and down so she could go to the bathroom.

At one point we were standing in the bathroom and I was helping her clean up again. She was holding herself up by leaning on me. She pushed herself away a bit and looked me right in the eyes. "I never meant for you to have to take care of me this way. I never wanted you to have to do this. No child should become the parent."

I tried to make light of the moment by saying, "I probably owe you this for a diaper change or two." But we ended up crying and hugging. Mom never used the bathroom again.

By Monday morning, Mom was retaining fluid, but she felt better after they drained nine pounds from her stomach. The oncologist came for his daily visit, and he asked Dad and me to step outside.

"I don't know if she has three weeks or three months, but she's not going to recover," the oncologist said. "Her body's shutting down. Her liver's not working. I've ordered a morphine pump. You can press it every 15 minutes so she gets a dose."

Dad had this great look of pain on his face.

I started crying but choked out, "When can we take her home?"

"You can't. I want her in the hospital so I can manage her pain. Her needs are too great now to be at home. If she improves in the next few days, we'll discuss it then."

Looking back, I realize that he hadn't voiced what he knew—that Mom wouldn't be there in a few days.

Mom zoned out on us not long after the morphine pump started. She mumbled unintelligibly to herself and moved her hands up and down like she was putting dishes in the cabinets.

Occasionally, she would wake up enough to hear me ask, "Mom, why are you doing that?"

She mostly smiled, but once she snapped, "Leave me be. I need to do this, OK?"

It wasn't OK.

We called the family back in again. I made it clear up front that I couldn't guarantee a time of death. But I didn't want anyone having regrets for not being there.

By Wednesday, Mom was swelling again and the nurse hooked up oxygen to help her breathe easier. We kept the lights off because Mom liked it that way.

Our pastor dropped by for a visit that afternoon. He stood in the doorway and sighed. We were a pitiful sight. We weren't talking, just existing, waiting. He gathered the family around the bed and explained that Mom could still hear us. He led us in the most beautiful prayer, told Mom that we were with her and loved her, and that it was OK to let go. He explained to us that it was time for courage—we needed to touch her and tell her often that we loved her and she could let go. We all tried. We wanted her to be free of the pain. I understood this in theory, but I stumbled in the execution.

A few hours after the pastor's visit, Mom stopped breathing. When I realized what was happening, I panicked and yelled, "Mom!" Startled, she jerked and began to breathe again. At the moment Mom needed me to let go, I panicked and screamed for her to come back. I was still just a little girl, so scared of the future. And of course she heard my cry and came back, back to the pain.

That night was Mom's last. The room was dark. The oxygen machine kept up a steady hiss. My Dad crashed on a chair, finally giving in to the exhaustion. My brother sat with Mom, holding her hand and pressing the morphine button every 15 minutes. I watched them from the windowsill where I was curled up, trying to sleep, trying not to think, trying not to be ticked off because my Mom was dying and it wasn't fair. There was a tremendous thunderstorm raging outside, and the lightning flashed close by. The storm mirrored the rage within me, but that was okay. All that great rage and grief brought clarity. I could feel God's presence, His awesome power, His love. God was letting me know that it was OK to be mad, to be pissed at the world, and to be crazy with grief over the loss of my mother.

The next morning, the sun was shining and peace filled the room. We realized her breathing was slowing. My brother led the way, kissing Mom, telling her he loved her, telling her it was OK to let go. The rest of us followed, and I tried to mean it. Mom listened to us, and then she was gone. Just like that.

No matter how it comes, death is sudden for the ones left behind.

I am longing for blue
Blue skies
Blue water
Blueberries
Maine blueberries
Maine blue waters
Maine blue skies

I am longing for blue Maine
The long blue length of Maine days in June
Sun up on blue water by four
Maine summer hurries
Summer seconds matter in Maine

I am longing for blue
The blue perfection of berries
Wild and blue and melting on the tongue
In Maine in summer
Blueberry scones drowning in blueberry jam
Devoured on the shore of blue Maine water
In the hurried-up summer

Blues
By Donna Campbell

I am longing for blue
Maine things
Waiting here
In the long, slow white
Of winter

The Cruise
By Susan Boles

With short, careful steps, Irene and Nelson made their way to the car in silence. Always a gentleman, he opened the door for her. But before she slipped into the driver's seat, they paused in each other's arms and their eyes filled. They had expected the doctor's confirmation of cancer. Irene had wrestled the wretched disease into remission twice before. Now she no longer had the mental or physical stamina to suffer the ravages of surgery, chemo, and radiation. This was the final round, cancer already declared the victor. The doctor had given her a prescription for pain.

Nelson shuffled to the passenger's side, arthritis making each step painful. Irene did all the driving now because macular degeneration was slowly stealing his eyesight. For several years, Irene had been his eyes and legs, but as cancer robbed her of strength, she wouldn't be able to continue that role.

As they drove home, Nelson broke the silence. "Let's not tell the children yet."

"Definitely not. They'd just barge in and try to take over. They treat us like we're going on a hundred instead of ninety. They'd have us moved into Sunny Farms Assisted Living before we could say 'Boo.'"

"Think it's time for that cruise?" Nelson asked.

Irene glanced at him. "Ummm-hmmm. You?"

Once home, Irene put the kettle on for a cup of Earl Grey. They perused a pile of cruise brochures, as they sat at the kitchen table, sipping tea and nibbling chocolate-chip cookies.

After a while, Nelson said, "You've always been the queen of my life. Let's sail on the Royal Queen of the Seas."

Irene smiled. "OK. Where does it go?"

"Depends on when we leave."

She put her brochure down on the table. "We need to go soon."

"How 'bout two weeks from Sunday?"

"We can be ready by then."

Nelson continued reading his brochure. "It's a ten-day Alaska cruise."

"Perfect. We've never been there."

"Leaves from Seattle."

Irene moved closer to her husband. "How much is a cabin with a balcony?"

"You'll have to read the small print."

He moved the brochure closer to her. His blue eyes twinkling, he added, "For the cruise of a lifetime, why don't we splurge on the Owner's Suite?"

"We can't afford that!"

With bravado, Nelson said, "Who cares? We'll charge it!"

"But we've got to pay for airline tickets, too."

Shrugging, he said, "We'll put them on a different card."

Irene snuggled close to her husband. "Oh, we're being so naughty!"

"Fun, isn't it?"

They made a conference call to the children after the trip was finalized, mentioning only the cruise, not that Irene's cancer had returned. Their response was predictable. Rena, the oldest, said, "You're too old to go gallivanting up to Alaska all by yourselves. Wait 'til we can go with you."

When the couple didn't respond, Todd added, "Dad, lately you seem to have a habit of getting lost. Plus, you know your eyesight's failing, and your knees make it hard for you to get around."

Mike, the youngest piped in, "Mom, you're so frail. Can you take care of Dad on a long trip?"

Nelson responded, "We'll be on a ship, for gosh sakes. How lost can I get? And besides, they have a doctor on board, should either of us need one."

Todd said, "We just can't let you do it."

With calm, steady voices, just like they had practiced, the elderly couple answered in unison, "We're going. End of discussion."

Nelson continued, "Now, we'd love to see all of you before we go. Can you drive out for a visit and take us to the airport next Sunday or shall we arrange for a taxi?"

When Irene and Nelson first entered the Centrum of the *Royal Queen of the Seas*, a jazz quartet was playing "It Had to Be You."

Nelson bent toward Irene. "Listen to what they're playing."

"Our song." She touched his cheek. "Must be a good sign."

In awe, they looked up at more decks than they could easily count. Passengers looked down at them, leaning against scalloped white balconies trimmed with polished brass railings.

"It's even prettier than it looked in the brochure," Irene said.

Nelson took a breath. "It's so big. We may be lost half the time."

Irene squeezed his hand. "At least we'll be lost together."

A young man, whose name tag indicated he was from the Philippines, greeted them so warmly, they felt like celebrities. He gave them their room passes, escorted them to the elevator, and pushed 10. Their suite was on the highest cabin deck.

A moment after they entered 1066, their cabin steward appeared and showed them everything they needed to know about their suite, assuring them he'd be at their beck and call 24 hours a day.

They had been on just one other cruise before and stayed in a tiny inside cabin, so they were thrilled with the expansive, well-appointed space of their living room, dining area, bedroom, and bath.

Nelson walked over to the whirlpool. "I don't know how in the devil I'll ever get in and out of the thing, but you and I are getting in there for a long soak at least once."

Irene laughed. "Guess what? I even brought some bubbles."

Nelson drew her close. "There's just one thing I don't like about the Owner's Suite, the king-sized bed. I'd rather have our double back home."

Nodding, Irene answered, "I hope we can find each other."

"I'll always find you, anywhere in the universe."

They walked out on the balcony and marveled at the view of Seattle's harbor. Ferries moved in the distance, while yachts went to and from the docks.

Nelson took her hand. "Can you believe we're here? Best thing we've ever done!" He kissed the top of her white curls.

Irene stretched on tiptoes, offering lips, which her husband eagerly accepted. Then she said, "All the travel and excitement have worn me out. I'm going to rest up for dinner."

With concern in his voice, he asked, "Do you need one of your pills?"

She nodded.

Even though they carried the map of the ship in hand, for the first several days they had to ask people for directions before finally locating the dining room. At dinner, the maître'd assigned them to a table with six other seniors, but they were by far the oldest couple and it won them celebrity status. They couldn't even drink all the wine offered to them.

When Nelson ordered from the menu, he stuck to plain old meat and potatoes, but Irene was adventurous. She tasted melon soup and fried octopus for the first time in her 88 years. If she didn't like something, the waiter hastened to bring her a second choice. Their hardest decision each evening was choosing what to have for desert, but the cakes and mousses, or anything with chocolate, became their standard selections.

Irene's stamina waned and the couple began to spend more time in their cabin, especially once they realized room service was available. Their dinners in the dining room satisfied their need to socialize. They had come on the cruise to spend time with each other, not others. They marveled at the glaciers and fjords from the comfort of their living-room sofa. When the ship docked, they observed the excitement below from the warmth of their suite.

The only excursion they took was one back in time, as they sailed down each thread woven into the tapestry of their lives together. Most of the fabric that made up their marriage was vibrant and vivid, yet there were dark, shadowy areas, and even some places where it had come apart. They felt compelled to erase the flaws in the tapestry. Courageously they reentered the dark years when Nelson had strayed into other beds and Irene had totally immersed herself in church, committees, and their three children. She had cut Nelson out of her life. The old drama captured the elderly couple in its net once again. Hurt, rejection, and blame flooded into their suite. They yelled at each other. Irene wept and Nelson sulked, until first one and then the other could say, "I was wrong. Please forgive me."

The walls of cabin 1066 heard Irene and Nelson reweave their tapestry over and again, until it was whole, bright, and beautiful. The couple learned that to forgive but once does not restore a violated beauty. They forgave each other over and over, 70 times seven times. Then they each had to forgive themselves an equal number.

Decades ago, Irene's first bout with breast cancer had brought them back together. The wretched disease made them realize how precious they were to each other. Now the uninvited guest was back, reminding them again that God meant them to be as one, inseparable. The sand in their hourglass was almost spent.

One day toward the end of the cruise, Irene woke up from her afternoon nap and discovered that Nelson wasn't anywhere in the suite. At first, she was angry he had gone out alone. A bit later when he still hadn't returned, she got worried and called both the Guest Relations desk and their cabin steward to tell them he must be lost. They promised to be on the lookout for him. Not knowing what else to do, she read her Daily Word and prayed.

A half hour passed before there was a knock at the door. There stood a member of the ship's crew with her husband, a frantic look in his eyes, biting his lips, clenching and unclenching his hands.

"Thank you so much." Irene murmured to the crew member.

She took Nelson into her arms and led him to the sofa where they sat a long, long time.

"It was awful," he said. "I couldn't find my way back."

Stroking his face, she said, "It's OK now. We're together again."

"It was like our cabin just disappeared."

"Where did you go?"

"Down to listen to music. When I left the music, I got on the elevator and punched ten. That's right, isn't it?"

Welcoming the opportunity to give him positive feedback, she answered, "Yes, we're on the tenth deck."

"When the elevator stopped, I turned the usual way and walked down the hall. Ten sixty-six wasn't there, so I had to walk all the way down the hall on the other side of the ship. By then, my legs were aching so much I could hardly shuffle along, even though I was putting most of my weight on the railing."

"Is that where the crewman found you?"

"No, when I walked past an elevator, I got on and punched a number. I . . . I don't know where I went. I got so confused." Through tears, he said, "I was afraid I'd never see you again."

"I'm here now. Nothing will ever separate us."

"I can't live without you."

"We'll be together forever, my sweet Nelson." Irene continued to comfort her husband, stroking his hands and arms. Eventually, he drifted off to sleep.

When he awakened, Nelson seemed to have forgotten that he'd ever been lost, but the stress had exhausted Irene. After dinner in their suite, the couple fell asleep on the sofa watching an old movie and holding hands.

At dinner on the last night of the cruise, Irene and Nelson insisted on buying wine for their table, a thank-you for their new friends' generosity on other nights. The evening became even more festive when the lights dimmed and the waiters paraded around the dining room with flaming baked Alaska.

Afterwards, they took in the final show in the auditorium. Even though the couple dozed through a good part of it, when it was over they exuded about how wonderful the singing and dancing were.

They were determined to do it all on the last night and went to the piano bar to toast both the cruise and themselves with a Brandy Alexander. The constant parade of the latest styles fascinated them and they marveled at the energetic dances of younger passengers.

Finally, the pianist played a slow song. Nelson placed his hand on top of Irene's. "They're playing our song. If you'll help me out of this chair, I'd like to dance with the most beautiful woman here."

With Irene's support, Nelson stood up. Slowly, they moved to the dance floor and began to sway to the strains of "It Had to Be You."

"It had to be you, my Queen Irene. Couldn't have enjoyed all these years with anyone else."

She turned her face up to Nelson. Her husband drew her closer and bent his head to place his lips upon hers. Lost in a lingering kiss, they stopped dancing.

"Only you," they both said as they began to sway again. Their eyes glistened as the song ended.

Adoration shining from his eyes, Nelson said, "Let's go back to our suite."

He beckoned his wife to bed. She was wearing the royal-blue nightgown and negligee that he had given her for Christmas. She slipped into bed beside him, both of them lying on their sides as close to each other as they could get. After a while, Nelson gently stroked Irene's cheek and ran his fingers back and forth across her lips. Slowly his hand moved to her breasts and across her nipples.

"What are you doing, you lovable old man?"

He sighed as his hand caressed her hips and made its way to the flower he had first picked a little more than 67 years ago, a whole month before their wedding day. Irene's mother would have been furious, had she known.

"I want to remember every inch of you forever and ever."

She caressed her husband as he kissed her. Then her fingers played with his short white moustache and slowly moved to his chest. The hairs there felt pleasingly rough.

Her hand made its way under the elastic of his silk pajamas and to the appendage that had enticed her for so many years.

"What are you doing, my sweet Queen Irene?"

"I'm appreciating everything you've meant to me all these years: body, mind, and soul."

Their mouths met for a long kiss, their tongues intertwining.

Nelson was the first to speak. "To think we've been in love so many years. Shall we go home together, my Sweet?"

"It's time," Irene said, gently touching his cheek.

They left the bed and made their way to the balcony, their arms entwined. When Nelson opened the door, a cool breeze made them shiver. They climbed on to the two chairs they had placed next to the railing that afternoon. The elderly couple bent toward each other and kissed once more. Holding hands, they leaned toward the dark, cold waters below as the last grain of sand passed through the hourglass.

Reunion
By Millard R. Howington

Not a planned deal, but enough
of us would show up on a Sunday
afternoon at the little white house
on a hill in Georgia with its massive
oak tree guarding the circular drive.
That rusting temperature gauge was
still nailed to the tree trunk and didn't
keep the temp anymore, of course, a
chewing tobacco ad fading with time.

A lovely young relative made the mistake
of walking in front of the floor fan and
her dress flew up just enough to reveal
a little leg and she let out the appropriate
demure yelp, retreating and smoothing
things back into place.

Something was different this time,
someone was missing and I inquired, much
to my regret. Uncle Leroy, with the glass
eye, recounted Cousingate to me: one
cousin's husband had been rendezvousing
with another cousin's wife, and there had
been fisticuffs and scenes and such, and
that's why they weren't there. The cousin
husband of the scandal had always been the
one to say grace before our Sunday group
dinners, with his trembly faltering voice, which
reminded me of someone verging on a nervous
breakdown. This time an understudy had to
fill in for him. I missed cousingate's sincere
prayer tremolo and knew, somehow, that
things would never be the same around there
again. They all lived much too near.

Paradise Found?
By Lynne M. Hinkey

July

Tracker knew what was coming an instant before the smell assaulted him. The slick squish under his flip-flop gave it away. "Aw, shit," he muttered. Then it hit him. Full blast in the nose, so thick he could feel it settling into his pores. The stench would stay with him for the rest of the day. "Damn mangoes."

He would cut down the tree in a heartbeat, but every time he mentioned it, there was an uproar from the marina's boaties. "It's so exotic!" But they could go back to their boats and breathe in the fresh salt air. The trade winds, blowing steadily from the east, pushed the sour odor of overripe mango away from their boats and straight into the marina office.

"If I never see or smell another mango again, it'll be too soon," he grumbled. Of course, it would just get worse now. The mangoes would ripen and fall nonstop throughout July and into early August, just as the trade winds slowed. The entire boatyard would fill with their sickly, too-sweet and too-sour stench.

"Hey Boss-mon, why you go an' mash up de mango dem? Pick it up an' eat it, mon, i' might sweetin' you up," his Rastafarian boat mechanic shouted to him. The mechanic was slouched low on a roughly nailed-together bench, melting into the back and seat, becoming one more not-quite-right angle with the scraps of wood and fiberglass. He picked up a mango from the ground, pulled back a strip of the bitter skin with his teeth, and sucked noisily on the stringy pulp around the giant pit.

"Don't you have anything better to do than lie around out here, Alberto? What about the lift truck? Have you fixed that yet?"

Tracker slammed the office door behind him. "Tropical paradise, my ass. I can't wait to get offa this Third World, godforsaken, hell-hole of an island!"

He picked up the real-estate magazine from his desk and eyed the aerial photo of the marina and boatyard. "Dream come true for enterprising business man/woman wanting to escape the rat race," read the caption. The marina had been on the market for 18 long months.

"I gotta get me a better real-estate agent," he growled.

Sitting down, he rifled through the stack of mail on his desk. "Bill, bill, return-to-sender, deadbeat boat owners." He sorted the envelopes into piles on his desk. "Bill, environmental regulation crap. . . ."

Tracker spotted a trail of orange, pulpy footprints tracking across the office to his desk. The smell of rotting mango reached his nose and his lip curled in revulsion. He remembered when the smell had seemed exotic, hinted at sultry tropical nights filled with mystery. He laughed bitterly. "I can't wait to get back to the real world!"

* * *

August

Tracker discreetly scooped up the pile of bills and late notices from his desk and slid them into a drawer. "It's a real moneymaker," he said, "practically runs itself. The boaters come in, hand over their money, and that's that. The dock master takes care of anything they need. Most of them are pretty self-sufficient—they do their own maintenance, and even help out keeping up the boatyard."

"What about the boatyard? I mean repairs and all. I don't know much about that. Sailing's just a hobby. Living on a boat has always been a dream of mine, and owning a marina is, well, that's even beyond my wildest dreams." When he'd been downsized, George put his severance package to good use, buying the 33-foot Bene-tau sailboat he'd coveted for the past five years.

"No problem. Our mechanic, Albert, takes care of everything." He looked out the window beyond George's head. "Yep, Albie's always on top of things." He watched as the mechanic glanced around the boatyard then followed a leggy blonde up the ladder onto her dry-docked sailboat.

"So, the dock master takes care of the docks, the mechanic takes care of the boatyard, the secretary handles the day-to-day business. What does that leave for the owner?" George asked.

"You, my friend, schmooze with the boaters down in the bar. Maybe show up at the monthly marina association meetings. Enjoy life in the tropics."

Tracker prided himself on his ability to size up boaters by the names of their vessels. When George sailed in on the *Wet Dream*, Tracker knew it was his lucky day. Everything about George and his brand-new boat screamed midlife crisis with an overactive libido (and, in Tracker's estimation, an overambitious one). As Tracker well knew from his own misspent middle-age, a man in that position was just a small nudge away from becoming a marina owner in the Caribbean.

"Well, it sounds too good to be true," George said. "Why would you want to sell?"

Tracker fingered the airline ticket under the stack of papers on his desk. Looking down, he saw the header "Johnson, Read, & Tavares, Attorneys-at-Law" boldly printed on the sheet of paper on top of the pile. He quickly moved his day planner to cover it. "You know how it is. My wife has island fever. She said either the marina goes or she does. Let me tell you something, it was a hard choice." He gave George a big grin and shrugged.

"I know how that is. Went through a messy divorce a few years back myself. My luck seems to have changed for the better ever since. But, I shouldn't tell you that." George winked at him. "You might change your mind."

"Yes, I'll miss this place. I've had some times here."

Tracker recounted stories about the marina and island life, knowing full well that George wasn't listening. From the half-smile playing on his lips and the faraway look in his eyes, Tracker knew his target's mind was on fruity tropical drinks with umbrellas in them, and sunsets from the deck of a gleaming white sailboat.

That's what all these daydreamers think life on a tropical island is like, Tracker thought. They don't know about the crazy obstacles paradise throws at you: overzealous environmental-enforcement officers, underzealous employees, corrupt politicians, and whiney marina patrons. All that laid-back, changes in latitude crap was all well and fine for Jimmy Buffet, he never tried to run a business here! But, if all went according to his plan, that would be George's problem soon, not his.

"Have we got a deal, Mr. Marshall?" Tracker asked, bringing George back from his daydreams.

"Deal." George stuck out his hand.

Out the window, Tracker saw his dock master stumble out of the bar. "You just bought yourself one hell of a marina, my friend."

* * *

February

George woke to the gentle lapping of water against the hull. The early-morning sounds of the marina waking up came through the porthole: tings and pings of the rigging, bird calls, and a few subdued voices from neighboring slips.

Coffee first, then I'll stroll over to the bar for some breakfast: a cheese-and-sausage omelet and toast, maybe some bacon, too. He felt the need to celebrate. It had been a rough six months, but things were finally turning around. The marina was almost full, the wastewater-treatment plant was fixed, the dock master had showed up for work every day this month, and Albie finally fixed the lift truck.

The lift truck had been a source of angst for George from the start. According to the mechanic, it had a "jumbie"—a trickster spirit that caused it to start up and run on its own. In the past six months, the mechanic had replaced the transmission and starter, changed and topped off every fluid in the engine, and put in new brakes. There hadn't been an incident in weeks. Maybe the insurance company wouldn't cancel the policy after all.

George put the coffee on, poured himself a Bloody Mary, and went up onto the deck.

The trade winds pushed a few puffy white clouds along in a soft blue sky. Sleeping white herons and snowy egrets dotted the mangroves along the shore. THIS is what life in paradise is all about. Now that things are running smoothly, I can finally kick back, relax, and reap the rewards of being a marina owner.

"George!" The dock master was rushing down the dock. "Hey, those guys from Conservation are here. Said they need some samples." He pointed to two uniformed men leaning over the end of the next dock filling glass bottles with water.

"Great," George muttered. "But the wastewater system is fixed, so we should be OK, right?"

The dock master shrugged. "You know, I've been meaning to talk to you about that—"

"Not until I've had my breakfast." He groaned and stalked off down the dock, bare feet slapping on the wood planks.

The bartender greeted him as he sat down at the bar. "Just the man I needed to see. The cistern ran out of water so I called for a truck. They'll be here soon. It'll be about four hundred dollars."

"Four hundred dollars for water?" George gaped.

"It's OK. They take checks."

A loud crash from the direction of the parking lot brought George to his feet. He ran from the restaurant, the dock master and bartender on his heels. A few heads poked out from vessels' hatches, looking for the source of the commotion.

The sight of the lift truck, halfway embedded in the side of a car—his car—brought George to a halt. "Albie?" he whispered, afraid to look under the wheels of the truck.

"Yeah, Boss." The Rastafarian boat mechanic jogged up. "Oh, shit. It got away, Boss. You know how she is — temperamental."

"I thought you said you fixed it."

"No, Boss. What I said was 'she's not acting up anymore.' I guess she is again."

George palmed the crown of his head. Only a few months ago, he could still touch the remaining fringe of hair around his ears when he did this. Where had it gone? He swore under his breath. I was mistaken, he thought. THIS is what life in paradise is all about.

* * *

April

Tracker tugged the sleeves of his Dale of Norway sweater down over his fingertips. He wanted to shout, "Shut the goddamn door," but instead he forced his lips into a smile. "Welcome to the Alpine Chalet. How can I help you?"

He'd had enough of snow, bitter cold, and snooty skiers to last him a lifetime. It had all seemed so easy when he got here. Rent or sell hiking gear all summer, ski and snowboarding equipment all winter. "The four cabins practically rent themselves," the previous owner had assured him.

He'd failed to mention the through-the-roof taxes, the Chamber of Commerce extortion, and the tree-hugging freaks on the town council, or the fact that winter lasted 10 whole months in this godforsaken place. Hell had indeed frozen over and it was now called Telluride, Colorado.

The man at the door held it wide, letting the bitter wind blow in. Four children, ranging from a toddler to a teen, straggled in and ran in four different directions. Still, he didn't close the door. Finally, a petite woman sauntered in, her face hidden behind giant dark glasses. Diamonds and gold glittered on every inch of her not wrapped in fur. She pulled her glasses low on her nose and sneered over the top. After giving a quick glance around and a small shiver, she nodded.

"Trophy wife," Tracker muttered.

The man finally let the door close and stomped a trail of gray muck up to Tracker. "The kids need some snowboard equipment. I don't see the appeal in it, myself. They have perfectly good skis. The sign says you offer instruction. They'll need that, too." He slapped a credit card down on the counter.

Tracker grabbed the two-way radio and called one of his ski instructors out on the slopes. At least that's what they called themselves. Bunch of lazy, good-for-nothing bums is what they were. More interested in picking up snow bunnies and drinking Jack Daniels than working.

The family was outfitted with their equipment and given directions to the slope where they'd meet the instructor. Tracker waved them out the door and immediately lost his smile. "God, I hate the cold. This is ridiculous—it's freakin' April!"

He picked up the real-estate magazine and gazed at the full-page color ad of the month's featured property, a souvenir shop in the Florida Keys. "Tropical dream come true for enterprising business man/woman wanting to escape the rat race," it read.

Tracker folded over the corner of the page.

A Toast to the Dead
By Brenda Bevan Remmes

Forty years ago in a village in Cameroon, West Africa, one of my students died. Not being on a friendly basis with death, I made numerous excuses to avoid the trek to accompany the body to its home village. Bernadette, a very bright 14-year-old who was living with me at the time, remained insistent.

"He knows what you're doing," she warned me. In some unexplained way, she was convinced that my absence would be an insult. So despite my uneasiness, I acquiesced and went.

The walk was only a few miles. The body was wrapped in a cloth and carried with us. Immediately upon our arrival, friends and family dug the grave and lowered the body into the ground. Words were said that I didn't understand. The grave was filled. The grief-stricken family seemed grateful that I was there, and I left knowing that Bernadette had been right.

As we departed, Bernadette took food she had prepared and placed it on top of the grave. When we arrived home, I couldn't help but ask, "Bernadette, why did you leave food on the grave? Do you think the boy will come up and eat it?"

She smiled and shrugged her shoulders in an uncomfortable gesture. "What do you put on your graves?" She asked.

"Flowers," I responded.

"So, you think he'd come up and smell them?"

I have told that story a number of times over the years and laughed at Bernadette's accurate response to my lack of cultural sensitivity. I was more respectful several years later while living in Ghana, West Africa, when a friend explained to me the purpose of libations. This is the practice of pouring a bit of your drink on the ground before taking the first swallow, in memory of those no longer living. It's similar to a toast: "Here's to you, Dad."

When my father died, he was 75 years old and left us with many wonderful memories that we still cherish. He was proud of his strong Welsh heritage, and in true Dylan Thomas fashion, he could "not go gentle into that good night," but "rage(d) against the dying of the light." It was not an easy death, but perhaps one that helped his family come to accept it sooner than he. We miss him.

Every morning on my way to work, I drive by the country home that he and my mother shared, and a short two miles up the road I pass the church where he is now buried. As was my custom during his life, I continue to beep twice each morning when I pass Mother's house, just to say "hello." But the first day upon returning to work after his funeral, I found myself starting to beep twice, also, when I passed the church.

Why was I doing that? Did I think he could hear me? No, of course not. I don't even think of him in the grave. I shrug my shoulders and laugh to myself as I ponder the question. So why do I do it? I don't know. I guess it's more of a salute, a libation. It's a toast each morning, and the sight of the church reminds me. "Here's to you, Dad."

In the evening after work, I stop by to share the news of the day with Mother. As I pass the church, I blow a kiss in that direction. As I do, I can hear Bernadette's quizzical voice. "So, you think he knows what you are doing?"

I smile in amusement at how wise I've become over the years.

"Yes, Bernadette, I think he knows."

Stephen Post Queen, February 26, 1894
By Brittany Vandeputte

MORNING
The strangling angel of children
Took my Margaret before sunrise.
And all the long way into town
I thought about the miseries I'd endured.
Crippled at one year with erysipelas.
At 13, a teamster for the Union army.
I carried the dead and wounded from Boteler's Ford.
Witnessed the ambush at Rich Mountain.
Nothing compared to the sight of that child,
Not yet seven months,
Lifeless in her cradle, her mouth pale and slack.

AFTERNOON
Mr. Haines normally charged five dollars for a casket.
Today he wanted three.
"I can't profit none from babies dying," he said.
I thought of my sister's children.
Willie, James, Esley, Abbey, and Sarah.
The angel'd come for three the month before.
And of my Nelly,
Just two years old
Pale in this morning's candlelight,
Struggling to breathe.
"Hurry back, Daddy," she told me.

NIGHT
Through stinging snow I rattled home.
Unhitched Honor from the wagon.
Put him and the casket in the barn.
The house was newly scrubbed.
Zinc sulfate, carbolic acid, water.
Eyes dark and wearied from the tears,
Ginny said, "Nelly's asking for you."
The little rosebud face
Barely rustled from the pillow.
"I've been waiting all day," she rasped.
"I wanted to tell you goodbye."

Long Silky Black Hair
By Donna Higgons

Colonel Huffington looked up to see Keiko being escorted through his door. *The war has been kind to her,* he thought and quickly looked back down at the pile of papers he was signing. "Come in. I'll be right with you."

He took a slow, deep breath to calm his nerves but the familiar aroma of Chanel No. 5 filled his nostrils and he chanced a look. His eyes took in her trim waist outlined by a navy-blue suit, gold buttons perfectly aligned, bulging slightly at her tiny breasts. She stood in front of the broad expanse of army-issue gray steel that was his desk. He knew Keiko wouldn't sit.

Colonel Huffington laid the last page on the pile, shuffled them into a neat stack, and handed them to the sergeant waiting at ease beside him.

"Here, Sergeant. See that Captain Jessup gets these processed immediately. We want these people back in their homes as soon as possible."

Taking a deep breath and standing up, Colonel Huffington forced himself to look straight into Keiko's black almond eyes.

"You look well, Keiko."

"Thank you, Colonel. A little older but a lot wiser," she said without a smile.

"Have you settled back home?"

"Our store was sold to Hawaiians. My parents and I—we live with auntie in Honolulu."

"I'm sorry, I didn't know." He cast down his eyes as he walked out from behind the desk. "Please sit . . . please." He gestured to one of the two upholstered arm-chairs designed to make interviewees feel at ease.

Keiko sat, perching rigidly on the edge of the chair, shoulders back, head high, knees and navy pumps held tightly together. Her hands rested demurely on her lap. Her eyes followed him as he leaned on the edge of gray steel, trying for a relaxed demeanor he didn't feel. He let the silence envelope him before venturing to speak.

"I knew your father was no spy. But the FBI thought that his acquaintance with Kokichi Tsonaga was enough to detain him. I could do nothing, Keiko. Nothing! And it tore me apart."

"But Kokichi only came for medicines! Japanese medicines! He didn't trust Western medicines. My father knew nothing of his spying. For that we had our rights taken away."

"You were in a sensitive position as well. They couldn't take a chance. Where did you go?"

"They sent us to Oklahoma—Fort Sill. Nothing but harsh sun in summer and icy cold wind in winter. We were only allowed one suitcase each, and of course we didn't have warm enough clothes for the winters."

Keiko related this calmly, her face showing no emotion as if she were reading one of the documents she used to translate. Her eyes never wavered, but her voice took on an edge he'd never heard before.

He stood up and walked behind her to the window where a carafe of ice water had been placed on a straight-legged, brown table. She did not turn her head to follow him and for that he was grateful. He stared out the window at palm trees bending away from an approaching squall and let his mind wander.

Keiko was the one who had kept him sane after Pearl Harbor, when he dealt with death and turmoil day in and day out. Her hands would knead out the knots in his shoulders, working down his back until he turned over and pulled her to him. His fingers would run through her black hair, arranging it to drape around her white shoulders. Then—with no warning—she was gone.

He shook his head to clear it and turned around. His eyes caressed the silky black hair cascading down her back. Hair he wanted to touch now with a fierceness that surprised him.

"Would you like a glass of water?" he said to her back.

"No, thank you. I only came about the job. This is a favor I must ask of you."

He watched her head bend down in shame.

"I have your application but if you came to work here it wouldn't be good, Keiko," he said. "I . . . I couldn't have you working in this office." He paused and—as if talking to himself—continued in a low voice, "I wish it was different."

Keiko stood up and turned to face the colonel. Her body softened as she reached back to lean on the desk behind her. "Butch, I understand. But General MacArthur is in Japan and he's looking for translators. My grandparents are there—not far from Hiroshima. It is my duty to help them if they are still alive. Can you get me a job there?"

He thought for a minute before replying. "I might be able to, Keiko. It's the least I can do. Call me tomorrow and I'll try to have some news for you."

"Thank you, Butch." She pushed away from the desk and walked to the door. As she turned the knob, she looked back, and with a catch in her voice she said, "I didn't know who else to turn to."

As the door closed softly behind her, Colonel Huffington poured himself a glass of water and downed it in one gulp like the tumbler of scotch he wished he had right now. He strode to his desk, picked up his briefcase and without even a glance at the pile of work on his desk, headed out the door. On his way through reception, the sergeant interrupted his departure.

"Sir! What do you want me to do with these orders to Tokyo?"

"Put them on my desk, Sergeant. I'll take care of them in the morning." He hurried out before the sergeant could ask any more questions.

Colonel Huffington slowly mounted the steps to his apartment. Reaching the stoop, he closed his eyes for a second, sighed, and opened the door. Once inside, he shut the door behind him, set his briefcase on the floor, and took off his hat, laying it on the table under the bamboo-framed mirror.

"I'm home, Yuriko!"

Yuriko came through the door from the kitchen and threw her arms around his neck, giving him a loud smooch on his cheek.

Butch untangled her arms from around his neck and looked into her sparkling black eyes. "I have good news and I have bad news. Which do you want first, Yuri?"

"Oh, Butch—the good news . . . the good news. The day has been too rainy for bad news. It can wait," she said, snuggling into his chest.

He pulled her close and worked his chin into the top of her head. He stared at their bodies reflected in the hall mirror.

"I'm being transferred to Tokyo to work with General MacArthur. There'll be a promotion in it," he said.

Yuri straightened up. "You'd better tell me the bad news, then."
His hand reached up to stroke her long, silky black hair.

Biscuits
By Brenda Bevan Remmes

It was the funniest sensation . . . biscuits.
That's what it was . . . biscuits.
I almost took it for granted.
I had heated the water and was washing off and I smelled biscuits.
Not just any biscuits, mind you, but Grandmother's biscuits

Were you there when we climbed the stairs that night?
Dickie, Cheryl, and I.
Uncle James and Aunt Edith were gone for the weekend
And Dickie had cut off the main light switch.
But there was a bet riding on it and Cheryl and I were determined
To make it through a night at Rip Raps.
We amused Dickie, if nothing else, and kept his mind
Occupied those times we intruded on his island of tranquility.
Those were the days before babies and war.

There was this door at the top of the stairs,
Right next to the window fan she put in after so many years.
You always had to pass it to get to any of the other rooms.
I used to sleep there, I think,
Although I can only remember one night.
I pinched myself to make sure I was awake, but it was still there.
Holding a broom. It wouldn't go away.
Next morning Grandmother laughed and said she didn't believe in ghosts,
But Dickie did, and Cheryl did, and I later heard Grandmother did, too,
Certain kinds, that is.
She turned it into a storeroom.

Biscuits with grits and scrambled eggs.
Sitting down to breakfast at nine and getting up at 11.
Sneaking into Uncle Joe's room to wake him by
Trying to tear off the covers. He'd always chase us.
Once he even took me out into the ocean and threatened to drown me.
It was Cheryl who figured out he slept without anything on.
I never believed it, though.

Biscuits with melted butter and jam . . . a basketful
Before you knew they were 150 calories a piece.
And grandmother, always stately, poised, the true
Matriarch of the family. If you got up at six you would have
Crackers and cheese with her, although the crackers were always stale.
With eyes shifting from Grandmother to Cheryl and back to the biscuits
We overcame prose on how to be young ladies.
What do you think she meant? I don't know.
What did she say? Boy, were those biscuits good.

How the wedding ever came about, I'll never know.
There we were eating the icing rings out of the middle of cakes
And weathering sea-storms in the hammock and then
There was this wedding.
Was that the first time we realized we were leaving . . .
Dickie, Cheryl, and I?
That was before Guadalajara, Bokito, and DaNang.

Coming Home
By Kimberlyn Blum-Hyclak

It was 7 p.m. by the time my daughter and I came home from a stay in the hospital. I settled her on the couch and waited for the home-health nurse to arrive. Seated at the kitchen table, I massaged my forehead and coaxed my body to relax.

This was not a typical childhood visit due to tonsils, a broken bone, or other malady. Gabrielle, eight years old, had battled leukemia for the past year. It was our second fight with this disease, after a three-year remission. This hospital stay had not been a regularly scheduled visit for a round of chemo, the nursing staff anticipating our arrival by putting mints on Gabrielle's pillow. This time she did not arrive in her favorite jammies, eager to get checked in so she could wander the halls attached to her IV pole, stopping at the nurses' station to help with labeling or sorting. Chemo admissions lasted three days and were little vacations for my daughter and me. We slept in the same room, sometimes snuggling in the same bed. We watched TV and played games. But this visit had not been one of those times.

Gabrielle had awakened with a fever. A temperature of 101 meant an automatic trip to the clinic and a stay in the hospital. With the compromised immune system of chemotherapy patients, infections are a serious threat. I bundled her up, grabbed our prepacked bag, and drove the 90 miles to Columbia.

When this happened before, Gabrielle strutted into the clinic and announced her unscheduled visit. This time I carried her. Arms and legs hung limp like a rag doll's, her head lolling against my chest. As we approached the nurses' station, doctors and nurses stopped in mid-motion and mid-sentence, then scrambled to set up a quarantine room and make arrangements to transport her to the Pediatric Intensive Care Unit. Without taking her temperature, checking her lymph nodes, or drawing her blood, they knew my daughter was in serious condition.

Within the hour, we were in a private alcove of the PICU. Throughout the day, she drifted in and out of sleep—always her cheerful self when awake, but not aware of where she was or what was going on. At 11 p.m., I was gently, but firmly, told that I needed to go to the Ronald McDonald House to get some much-needed sleep. I was assured the staff would call if anything changed.

The call came at 1 a.m. I don't remember driving to the hospital. I only remember the look on her doctor's face when I made it back to the nurses' station. I couldn't go in and see Gabrielle; he had to talk with me first. They were prepping her for surgery, the surgeon already enroute. They were merely waiting for my consent. It appeared an infection had settled in her intestine and was becoming gangrenous, a major complication the doctors always watched for. One of the risks of operating was that once the cutting began and the infection exposed to air, it would spread rapidly. With no infection-fighting white cells, Gabrielle had no defenses. The doctor held me by both shoulders and made sure I looked at him.

"You need to know that her chances of

not surviving this surgery are far greater than her surviving it. Do you understand what I'm telling you?" Those words forever etched themselves in my memory.

I looked at him as the words sunk in, my stomach churning. "You're telling me I have to say goodbye to my daughter."

I had done this before. Years earlier, the first time through therapy, I'd held her in the early hours of another morning. I was convinced that if I laid her in bed, she would not wake. I rubbed my cheek against hers, my nostrils taking in her baby-lotion scent. I stroked the peach fuzz where long curls once grew. I embraced her tiny frame, needing to imprint the softness of her skin, her smell, the dead weight of her sleeping body. Then I offered her to God. If the only way to make her whole and healthy was to let her go, then God had my permission to take her.

He hadn't.

Now I wondered, after five years, was He accepting my offering after all? I had no right to say "no." I slipped into her cubicle. I wished she were asleep, but she greeted me when I entered. I told her she was going someplace with Dr. Kevin. I let her believe everything would be OK. My rationale was that if she survived, I'd see her again. If she didn't, she would be with God. Either outcome was easier to accept than saying the word. I caressed her face and held her as best I could. My last words to her were, "I love you."

The operation revealed no sign of gangrene or infection, but that guaranteed nothing. Yet, she survived and we watched as she slowly recovered. We rejoiced at every minor improvement.

When a resident remarked that her low white-blood count really wasn't all that good, we laughed. We knew she had *none* when she was admitted. After a few weeks, she moved to a regular room and after a few more, we came home. We'd been gone a month.

That night at the table seemed endless while living it, compressed into a moment of relief and thanksgiving. The nurse arrived, hooked up the new IV, monitored it for an hour, then left. The pump's low hum let me know it was running smoothly. The rhythmic clicking assured me that nutrients were being delivered in measured doses. These were sounds I'd grown accustomed to. Other muffled hospital noises were replaced by calls of the whippoorwill and owl in my woods. Gabrielle slept contentedly on the couch. I looked forward to sleeping in my own bed.

I settled in my rocker to read the local paper, the first one since we'd left. A headline jumped out at me, "Five Killed in Tragic Car Accident." A mom, her two children, and both children of another family were killed instantly, coming home from school. I read and reread the article. Each time I cried harder. I kept waiting for the names to disappear. I wanted them to fade and reappear as something other than the names of my friend's children.

Rosemary, the surviving mother, was Gabrielle's Brownie leader. Our daughters were in the same troop. During our month in the hospital, Rosemary sent pictures drawn by the rest of the Brownies. The night of her children's viewing, I went with pictures drawn by my daughter. As I entered, I saw a line of little girls, waiting. Rosemary knelt in front of one, her arms lightly around her. Rosemary's eyes were closed as she softly, barely, stroked the little girl's hair. The child stood perfectly still.

A sob caught in my throat and my heart ached for her. I knew what she was doing.

The memory of reading the paper that spring evening still haunts me. I'd held my daughter, fully expecting to never hold her again. Rosemary said goodbye to both her children, fully expecting to welcome them at the end of the day. Knowing her, I know her final words that morning were "I love you."

Rosemary and her husband eventually adopted two children, a boy and a girl, close to the ages of their first children when they died. Gabrielle, then 16, was their babysitter for a summer.

My new husband occasionally gets frustrated when I don't worry about things like he does. I can't. Twice I was pulled from the edge of that abyss that most parents fear. The weight and depth of everything else pales in comparison. And I've experienced how quickly things can change: in a few hours of the morning, in the brief moments of reading a headline, in the time it takes to come home.

From Match.com to Reelfoot
By Betty Wilson Beamguard

Wild-woman Diane arranged to meet a guy she found on Match.com, and worst of all, she dragged me into it. Diane's a good-looking gal—large, shapely, with warm brown eyes and honey-blond hair—and she has that certain something that attracts men. She wouldn't have to resort to online dating, but she's afraid Jerry will find out if she messes around with any of their friends, and she's hell-bent on messing around.

She came up with a plan to meet the guy in the northwest corner of Tennessee at Reelfoot Lake and asked him to bring a friend. She used me as an alibi. The line Jerry got was that I wanted to look for ivorybill woodpeckers. They're supposed to be extinct, but somebody spotted one in Arkansas a few years ago. Goofball Diane told Jerry I dreamed there was a pair nesting at Reelfoot and was obsessed with finding them. Making him think I was a nutcase didn't bother her conscience one bit.

Three hours into the drive up from Memphis that Friday finds us looking at flat farmland with water standing in ditches and plowed fields. The smell of damp earth drifts in the windows of Diane's silver Impala as we roll into Tiptonville past an abandoned factory with missing windows that look like rotted teeth. Across the highway stands singer Carl Perkins's boyhood home, which has never seen a coat of paint and looks as if it might collapse before year's end.

We whip in at the Dairy Queen for lunch. Sitting outdoors at a picnic table painted in primary colors, I lap my orange ice-cream bar like a contented puppy. "I haven't had one of these since I was a kid. Weren't they called Dreamsicles back then?"

Diane shrugs. "Beats me."

"Hey, Miss I've-got-all-the-bases-covered, you better pocket that wedding ring."

"Oops!" Diane snatches off her ring and throws it into her oversized bag.

"You should be ashamed, toying with this guy. I feel guilty being a part of it."

"Cool it with the guilt trip. I made it clear that I just wanna have a little fun, OK?"

We ask directions from an older couple sitting at the other table and head for the Air Park Inn. Diane arranged to arrive a day before the guys so we could check out the place. They're supposed to meet us for lunch on Saturday, April Fools' Day.

Riding north past more fields, we turn right at the sign. With little else around, we have no trouble locating the Air Park Inn. Its gray paint blends with the leafless trees that border the lake. We march up the entrance ramp, our roll bags bumping along behind us. At the desk, we pay, then push open the rear door that leads to the open concrete platform on which the rooms rest. We find our number and unlock the door only to be welcomed by the smell of stale smoke and pine cleaner. Diane is used to Jerry's cigarettes, but I nearly gag.

I slide open the glass door at the far end and ease onto the balcony to lean against the high plank rail. Murky water laps at the pilings below and spreads into open lake to the left, with nothing but woods lining the shore as far as I can see. Directly ahead, cypress trees stand in shallow water, their knees bumping up in irregular patterns. Small islands lie here and there, covered in brush and trees just starting to bud. A family of mallards swims past and a hawk cries out as it circles overhead.

The scene reminds me of the Louisiana bayous, minus the Spanish moss. It's peaceful, no humans in sight, but there's something sinister about the silence. It's the kind of quiet that, in movies, means a gator's approaching or somebody's about to get clobbered. A bald eagle skims the treetops.

I hear the toilet flush, Diane running water, then "Kit! Come look at this."

Poking my head into the bathroom, I focus on the hole to which she's pointing—a slot cut in the wall next to the sink. "What's that?"

Diane shrugs. "I think it's where you dispose of razor blades. My aunt had one in her medicine cabinet, back when everybody used straight-edge blades."

"Gosh, wonder how old this place is." I sniff. "You smell fish?" I track the odor to the bench across from the sink. "Gross! There are dried fish scales stuck on the wood."

"Forget that. Let's see what we've got here, girlfriend." Diane prances around, ticking off amenities. "TV, VCR, mini-fridge, coffeemaker, and flyswatter."

"You're kidding."

She picks up the red plastic swatter and slaps it against her palm. "Hey, this gives me ideas."

"You and your trashy mind. So, what do we do now?"

"Relax?"

"Good idea." Visualizing the hunters who might have stretched out on the bed, I decide not to lie directly on the spread. Instead, I crawl between the sheets for a nap while Diane flips through her *People* magazine.

About 3:30 p.m., we head back to Tiptonville, a typical Southern town with assorted shops in rundown brick buildings. We end up at the levee that runs along the Mississippi. Having gone as far as we can in that direction, we turn back to explore the section of Highway 21 that circles the lake, passing fishing lodges and family-run motels.

Diane whips the Impala in at the state park visitor center and I follow her inside. She flirts with the ranger, asking dumb questions as we meander among displays of local wildlife. On seeing live rattlers, a copperhead, and a cottonmouth, I drop my hiking plans.

Next stop, Boyette's for supper, right up the road from the diner where we're to meet the guys. I order the vegetable plate—baked apples, white beans, hushpuppies, mashed potatoes, slaw, and onion rings. It's like sitting down to my grandmother's table. I catch a few people eyeing us, maybe because we're not from around there, or because we're female. Reelfoot is definitely a guy kind of place, a sanctuary from women and children where men can drop a hook or sit in a duck blind all day, drinking and exchanging hunting tales. Even the restaurants reflect class and gender bias—down-home diners, a barbeque hut, a fish shack, a Sonic, and the good old Dairy Queen.

As the sun sinks lower, we follow the main road around the lake past more "resorts" and rustic motels. Without warning, Diane turns down a dirt road.

"Where're you going?"

"I'm gonna see where this takes us."

"I don't think this is park land."

"Who cares?"

I drop the conversation when we come upon a group of older men standing next to three pickups and two boats at the water's edge. They stop talking to watch us bump along the lane narrowed by trees and vines.

I turn to Diane. "Isn't one of the basic rules of online dating to meet in a safe location? This town, the inn, the whole place gives me the willies."

"Reelfoot was his idea—it's pretty much the halfway point between us. Besides, you know my motto: Rules were made to be broken."

"Yeah, that policy served you so well in high school. I swear, Diane, I liked you better when you drank. You were a lot more predictable. You seem to have this compulsion to fill your life with chaos. Drinking did that for you, but now it's like you have to seek out trouble."

"Look, you teach. You have your art, all your brothers and sisters and nieces and nephews. What have I got? A big new house and nothing to do, not even Jerry. If he's not working, he's out getting tanked."

"So get a life. Find a job. A hobby. Divorce Jerry."

"I don't have your education and I don't need a job. Jerry makes plenty now that he's construction boss. As for leaving him, if I had anything on him, I might. Every once in a while some friend will tell me about seeing him flirt with a waitress or a gal at a bar, but there's no name, nothing I can prove."

"Have him followed."

"You think I have a death wish?"

Up ahead, we spot a man getting into his truck. Like the group up the road, he eyes us, not lustfully, but suspiciously.

"We need to go back before dark."

"Soon as I find a place to turn around."

In a stretch of road with a few feet of grass on both sides, we circle and head out, passing the same geezers as before, enduring the same rapt attention. We drive back to the inn with night closing in. Just before we reach the parking lot, Diane has to brake for a possum taking its sweet time to cross the road.

As we walk up the ramp, we hear a sharp crack like rifle fire. Our heads snap to the right.

"Beaver," says a deep voice from behind a cigarette. "Come over here and you can see him."

We cross the deck and edge over to the rail. Barely visible in the twilight, a beaver bobs in the water as he chomps a water-lily bulb. I slap at a mosquito on my arm. The beaver answers with another smack of his tail on the surface of the water, then swims out of sight under the inn.

The tall man moves closer. "You seen their lodges?"

"No," Diane answers. "What do they look like?"

"Big piles of sticks. There's one right off the pier farther out—on this side."

"I bet we can see it from our balcony."

I elbow her, afraid she'll tell him our room number. "Let's go in. These mosquitoes are eating me alive."

The man stays to finish his cigarette while we hurry through the lobby, out the rear door, and back into semi-darkness. The platform is now lit by yellow bulbs set low along the railing, angled to shine inward so as not to disturb the wildlife in the inky water beyond.

Back in the room, I slide the balcony door closed against the chill. Diane fiddles with the clicker. "We don't have cable. That sucks."

"I'm not surprised, remote as this place is." I check my phone. No signal. I stretch out with *The Wind Came Sweeping*, the novel I'd brought along.

Next morning, equipped with cameras and binoculars, we drive around, this time heading away from Tiptonville. We spot turkeys, deer, herons, and ducks, and stop the car to watch a pair of young eagles fight over some mangled creature. The morning eases by.

Diane checks her watch. "Better head for the Lakeview Diner."

"Nervous?"

"Excited. But what are we gonna talk about? He's a tobacco farmer and likes to fish. I don't know beans about tobacco or bass."

"So why did they match you with him?"

Diane waddles her head back and forth and shrugs before admitting the truth. "I think I put something like 'I'm a country girl at heart' and maybe 'I like to fish.' Most guys fish, don't they? I figured that would improve the odds of getting hits."

"Don't expect any sympathy from me. You deserve whatever you get. How old did you say you were?"

"Thirty-eight."

"Six years ago you were thirty-eight!"

She grins as she pulls up to the diner. We tell the hostess a couple of guys will be joining us. While we wait, a new worry pops up.

"Diane, you're not planning to drink, are you?"

"Of course not. What made you think that?"

"You're pretty much going wild here, so how am I supposed to know what you will and won't do?"

"I almost went to jail. Do you know how scary that is? No, I plan to stay sober. Besides, he's a teetotaler. Wait until you see his eyes. They're green."

I stick a straw in my lemonade and twist its paper cover into designs until Diane grabs my wrist.

"That's them—the red bandana."

I turn to see a tall thickset guy with mostly-black hair and a short salt-and-pepper beard. He wears a bandana around his head and has his Harley T-shirt tucked under the belly that hides the waistband of his jeans. Beside him stands a wiry guy not much taller than I am, looking as frantic as a cornered mouse.

Diane jumps up to wave and they head our way. Sure enough, Diddle Dawson does have clear green eyes, but the lids stay at half-mast, giving him a lizard-like appearance. Even so, his eyes are definitely his best feature and the same can be said for Ed No-Last-Name. His eyes glow golden brown under long lashes.

We order, eat, and make small talk. Diane bats her mascara-coated lashes until I fear I'll lose my hush puppies. I thought they'd gotten acquainted by e-mail, but from the questions she's asking, I can tell they've done little more than agree to meet.

"How'd you get the nickname *Diddle*?" she asks.

He leers. "It's easier to show you than to tell you."

Diane giggles into her hand like a 13-year-old.

I wonder about Diddle's age. He has to be at least 55. I smell beer on Ed and judging by the way Diddle's acting, I'd say he's downed a few, too, despite his claims of abstinence. He shares tales of his wild exploits while Diane gives him her full attention, laughing in all the right places. I can tell she's faking, but that's Diane. She wants them to like her whether she likes them or not.

As I fork the last of my potato salad, I decide to set Ed straight early on. With Diane and Diddle exchanging inane innuendos on the other side of the table, I say, "Just so you'll know, I have a boyfriend." If Diane can lie, so can I.

Ed frowns and leans toward me. "What say?"

The restaurant is now full, the volume of the chatter annoying. I raise my voice to repeat what I've just said and add, "I just came along for the ride."

He gets this amused twitch at the corner of his mouth. I glance at the other two. Yep, they heard it, too. *Mortified* is too mild a word for what I feel at that moment.

Diddle scoots back his chair. "I'm paying. My treat."

Nobody tries to talk him out of it. At the counter, I pause to pick up a mint and see Ed reach for a toothpick. I notice a circle of white around his tan ring finger.

They've driven down from Paducah in Diddle's green Ford Ranger, so we step outside to make our first group decision—how to proceed with the date.

"Y'all wanna split up in couples?" suggests Diddle.

Diane hedges. "We can all ride in my car. Where're we going?"

"How about a movie? We could drive to Union City or Dyersburg. No theater here."

"I'm kinda tired from the drive, and I know y'all must be, too. Why don't we just hang around here. What is there to do?"

"Not much of nothin'," Diddle admits.

Ed and I listen while they settle on riding to the levee in the Impala. With country music on the radio, we head out of town. The headlights pick up a couple of deer, a raccoon scurrying through tall grass, and a car parked on the levee with no heads in sight. Although Diddle doesn't appear to possess extraordinary intelligence, it doesn't take him long to figure out Diane has no intention of parking. He gets quiet and lets a couple of yawns and a belch escape. Diane takes the hint and returns to the diner.

They follow us back to the inn where we turn down their invitation to join them in their room, as well as their offer to escort us to ours. We assure them we feel perfectly safe and with polite goodnights, walk off. The bam of their door startles me, though I can't say it wasn't justified.

As we pick our way along the platform with black night hanging beyond the railing like a wool blanket, I whisper, "Wanna head out before they get up tomorrow?"

"Sounds good to me. They're duds. I've got a couple more that look promising, though. I told you about Rob, didn't I?"

"No, you didn't, and don't even think about involving me again."

We reach our door and what I see next makes me wish we'd let the guys come with us. Printed on a napkin nailed to the door by a homemade wood-handled paring knife is a note: "YOU PLAY—YOU PAY."

Diane starts to tremble. "Jerry," she whispers.

"I thought he had to finish excavating the Wal-mart site."

"That's what he told me, but my granddaddy made me that knife and a butcher knife for me when I got married."

As we stand whispering in the shadows, so close I can feel her warmth, I look around, scanning for movement. "We need to get inside. Or do you think he's in the room?"

Diane checks the lock. "We could get the guys to go in with us."

"Forget that. I'll take my chances with Jerry." I stick the key in the lock, turn it, and shove. The door sticks. I throw my shoulder against it. The door pops open and swings into the wall with a bang. As it bounces back, Diane yelps and slams into my back full force. I go down. She crashes on top of me, squeaking and gasping. The door slams. I freeze.

Diane rolls off me, but huddles close, clinging. The light comes on. I look up to see Jerry towering over us, his fury making him seem twice as big. He's holding a butcher knife aimed down at us.

His right hand shoots out to haul Diane up. "Bitch! You whoring tramp of a wife."

Ignoring me, he rants as he drags Diane toward the bed. She whimpers, pleads for her life.

"Kill you? Oh no, baby, I'm not gonna kill you. But you're gonna be begging me to."

Trembling, I crawl toward the door. When Diane lets out a scream that shakes the night, I jump up and rocket out, yelling for help as I race down the row of rooms. A man in camo pokes his head out.

I halt and dash back. "Gun. Do you have a gun?"

I'd left the door open and Diane's next scream spurs the man to action. He grabs a hunting rifle and his buddy follows with a pistol. I point to the door and they rush in.

"Drop the knife!" yells the one with the rifle.

Jerry's head jerks around. Crazed with rage and who knows what substances, he stares for a long moment while we all hold our breath. He wavers, as if trying to focus, reprogram, catch hold of reality.

"Drop it and get off her."

This time, Jerry moves, slowly backing off the bed to stand with his back to the curtain that billows next to the balcony. He whirls, flings himself out the door, and scrambles over the rail. We hear a splash. The men rush out and fire into the dark, but he's already ducked under the concrete platform.

Behind me I hear "Damn." I whirl to see Diddle, Ed, and several other men.

I yell, "Go to the desk and have them call an ambulance."

Ed obeys, but Diddle rushes over to Diane. I grab his big arm. "Oh, no you don't. I'll take care of her."

The man with the pistol steps up. "I'm an EMT. I'll get the first-aid kit from my car. Use the sheets to apply light pressure to stop the bleeding."

Feeling faint, I press a wadded sheet into the wound below Diane's breast while the man with the rifle wraps the stab wound on her shoulder.

Word of the attack spread quickly and some locals caught Jerry when he staggered out of the swamp. Diane recovered from her wounds and got the divorce I'd suggested. While Jerry rots in prison, she's merrily dating the male friends she never dared mess around with before.

Jesus on a Bicycle
By Bob Strother

On Tuesday, I saw Jesus on a bicycle and
worried that his robe might tangle in the
chains. Foolish me. Things like that never
happen, do they?

A Tender Age
By Bob Strother

I lie awake in the darkness
remembering how my skin,
now paper-thin and creped,
once crackled under your touch.
How we lay intertwined,
sated and dozing;
a pool of sweat collecting
in your bellybutton as the
afternoon sun stole through
the blinds and painted fiery
streaks across our bed.

Time is a cunning thief,
stretching out of sight only
to reappear when we least expect it,
looming large over our shoulders.
Too late we realize
that the privileges of youth
are never surrendered;
they're simply taken from us.

Then I feel your arm
slide across my chest,
feel the warmth of your breath
on my neck, and I weep.

The Very Sick Passenger
By Kim Catanzarite

Less than an hour out of Atlanta, the pilot's voice drops like pebbles from the speaker above our heads. I look up from my magazine. He has already given the spiel about weather conditions, possible turbulence, and our distant ETA, so an announcement at present is cause for concern. Especially when he says something about a very sick passenger.

I imagine an old woman laid out on the floor, Free Spirits empathically removed. A glance down the aisle renders no information. Up front, the first-class curtain preserves the privacy of the well-to-do.

I elbow my husband, Joe. "Did you hear that?"

He nods, not bothering to open his eyes. He's trying to sleep, and so should I. We, the childless, are traveling to Russia, land of parentless children. We have money to deliver, a train to catch, a court date for an adoption that won't wait.

In other words, we cannot be late.

Ping! The pilot again: "Is there a doctor on board?"

A woman wearing heels and an air of authority ushers past the curtain into first-class territory.

"It must be pretty bad," I say. I blink once or twice and the woman reappears, striding the opposite way.

The pilot addresses us a third time, no evidence of annoyance in his voice. "It looks like we are going to have to stop at JFK so we can take care of our very sick passenger. We may or may not ask you to deplane while a safety sweep takes place and the condition of the aircraft is established—we're pretty heavy with fuel so damage may occur when we land." Pause. "And, of course, we want to make sure nothing is on board that shouldn't be."

Nothing on board that shouldn't be! Like a bomb in a suitcase? My face bursts into flame as I picture the plane doing the same. We live in a time of terrorism.

Joe takes my hand. I pray: *Please God, should we survive this flight, let us get to court on time.* I'd like to avoid the domino effect that will start with arriving late in Moscow and end with our going home, childless again.

An attendant ties back the first-class curtain. Nothing unusual going on up there as far as I can see. Just a boy of maybe three skipping down the aisle, a cherub smile plumping his cheeks.

We land without blowing up—and deplane. On the way to the "quarantined area," a passenger from first class tells us a child is sick—or its mother—no one's sure because the mother speaks a brand of Russian that the flight attendants cannot decipher. Plus, both the child and mother look fine. "It's all very suspicious," she says.

Why, I wonder, would anyone insist the flight crew land the plane when we just got off the ground? If this woman did not want to go to Russia, why did she board in the first place? Is she indeed a terrorist? Did she intend to leave behind a suitcase with a bomb—or worse, some easy-to-hide explosive microchip timed to detonate? The pilot and crew must consider her a threat. Why else would they give in to her demands and take her to JFK?

It was all very suspicious.

Meanwhile, my husband and I, amongst hundreds of passengers eager to get on with the 12-hour journey, are ushered like cattle through a tunnel that leads to an ordinary gate—except that this one is roped off with police tape. We must stay within the yellow boundary. Do not attempt to visit the restroom, do not scavenge for something to eat.

The sick mother stands in a separate glassed area—bellbottom jeans, fringy purse—while the rest of us watch the interrogation unfold like TV. The jaws of the TSA agents are set, their arms crossed over their chests. The woman wears her child like a shield. Lips move but we can't hear a thing.

Joe says, "I can't believe all of this is for one person."

Twenty minutes pass. I'm starting to worry we won't make it to Moscow on time, that we'll miss the overnight train to Kirov, that the court date will evaporate along with our opportunity to take home the child who we met the month before. The baby so close to being our own.

I hear a sound like bone hitting glass. The men in jackets descend. The mother writhes like a trapped animal. Clothing is stretched, skin exposed, shrieks emitted. The child is extracted like a stubborn tooth.

The murmuring of the crowd is silenced.

Then, an announcement: "Please have your passports ready, we will be boarding momentarily."

It seems too soon. I turn to Joe. "You think it's safe?"

He shrugs.

While we form a line to reboard, two agents wheel the sick mother, hands tied behind her back, through the crowd. She's kneeling atop a gurney, begging with her eyes. I'm waiting for a rotten tomato to nail her, an empty can of soda to bounce off her head, as they surely would have in less-civilized times. But not today. Today, the mood is one of stunned silence. And fear. Fear of the unknown.

Who is she and why did she do this?

"My child," she shouts, "they have taken my child!"

Is she a mother and a terrorist, too?

I don't know whether to curse or cry. But here I am, at the head of the line. The attendant reaches for my passport, places a checkmark beside my name. I do not want to get back on that plane. But I do want my child, the one waiting at the orphanage, the one I plan to love and protect. The one who has already claimed the daughter place in my heart.

And I can't be late.

I stumbled on them in the dark.
They spilled from their maze of holes,
bitter conversation burning at my throat.
Eight million pinprick letters
scatter up the ash-white newsprint
of my bare leg—
angry words march across paper—
their soul/sole purpose to hurt me.
How like them I am;
How confused I am by them—
their feet, infinitesimal,
burdened with fire and pain.
I think
I would like to hear their voices,
read the nuances
of movement and dance—
as if by loving them enough
their words will enlighten me.

The Fire Ants
By Robin Lewis

The Last Word
By Grace W. Looper

Hannah yawned and struggled to open her eyes. She'd slept later than usual because her sister, Bella, kept her awake with her moaning, saying she had a terrible headache. Bella ignored her suggestion to take something. Too bad the sisters must share a room, although it was large and had twin beds. Neither of them wanted to take over Papa's room when he passed away. Unfortunately, the house he left them had only two bedrooms.

If the saying opposites attract were true, it certainly didn't apply to Hannah and her sister. Mothers-in-law and daughters-in-law got along better than they did.

Hannah became reconciled to her appearance and personality a long time ago. Bella described her as tall and thin with a prune face—the epitome of an old maid. She wore her never-been cut hair in a huge bun on her neck, no makeup, and dark clothing that hid almost every inch of her age-spotted flesh. Bella took great delight at pointing out Hannah's shortcomings.

At 63, Hannah was three years older than Bella, who was pretty in an overblown way—slightly plump, big hair dyed a garish blond, protruding blue eyes, and pale skin she zealously protected from the sun. She'd married at 19 and moved out of the family home while Hannah stayed to care for their ailing father. Their mother died while they were in their early teens.

Hannah struggled up, fingers probing her aching head. She discovered Bella's bed empty and was surprised Bella had gotten up before her. In the bathroom, she frowned at the wet towel on the floor, hairs in the sink, and toothpaste splattered on the fixtures. Ordinarily, she would have tidied up, but this morning, suffering from a lack of sleep, she wasn't in the mood to be generous. She finished in the bathroom, folded her flannel gown and put it away, donned a black skirt and a long-sleeved white blouse, and made up her bed. Bella's bed was unmade and the clothes she'd taken off last night were strewn all over her side of the room. How could she have a sister who was such a slob?

Entering the living room, Hannah found Bella stretched out on the sofa with a damp cloth on her forehead.

"Oh, there you are, sister. I couldn't sleep because of this terrible headache. Would you be a dear and bring me a cup of coffee, toast, and maybe an egg and slice of bacon?"

"No, Bella, I won't. I don't feel well this morning. I couldn't sleep for your moaning. If you're able to eat, then you're able to fix what you want. After you've eaten, I suggest you clean the mess in the bathroom and your side of the room. I'm through straightening up after you."

"Ouch! You're in a dreadful mood. How can you be so mean to your suffering sister? I'll get to my room on my time. I don't live by a rigid schedule like you."

Hannah turned her back on Bella. How she hated it that Bella always managed to have the last word. No matter how long she prolonged the conversation, Bella made a final retort. She held her hands over the stove. "You've opened the damper again. How many times have I told you we can't afford to buy so much wood?"

"But I was cold."

"No wonder with that disgraceful gown and robe you're wearing. Why can't you get dressed? You look like a floozy."

"I like to be comfortable, especially when I don't feel well."

"What if we have visitors?"

With a rueful laugh, Bella retorted, "We don't have visitors."

"Reverend Simmons comes about once a month."

"Whoopee! He always calls before he comes, and I dress in my most respectable outfit to please you. Just look at you now. You're the picture of the old maid you are. That blouse is so stiff with starch, I don't see how you can turn your head. It wouldn't do for a few inches of your neck to show. I found a husband and there were a few more waiting in line for my hand. I had a choice."

"Some choice you made. Justin was flashy and outwardly charming, but it didn't take you long to find out that he was addicted to drinking and gambling."

"At least, I know how it is to be with a man. I don't believe you've ever had a date. Has a man ever kissed you?"

It was hopeless. Bella always got back at her in some hurtful way. Would she ever have the last word? Hannah got a glass of water and downed two aspirin. Their constant bickering had made her headache worse. She went into the kitchen, made a pot of strong coffee, poured herself a cup, then relented and poured one for Bella. She added cream and sugar to Bella's and carried them to the living room. "Here."

"So you're feeling guilty for being mean to me." Bella took a swallow. "Ouch! It's too hot and doesn't have nearly enough sugar."

"It wouldn't hurt you to lose a few pounds."

"Nonsense. Men like a nice armful. Hugging you would be like hugging a suit of armor—all those hard, sharp bones."

"I do believe you're out to get another husband with all this talk of men, and at your age, too."

"Why not? I'm sixty and look forty. It would do you good to think about men a little instead of keeping your nose in a book all the time."

With a pounding head, Hannah turned away. Maybe a little food would help. She fixed a bowl of cream of wheat and added cream and sugar. It always soothed her stomach. She ate slowly, wondering what to do with Bella. She suspected she had a hangover. One glass of sherry before dinner didn't satisfy her. Finishing eating, Hannah checked the cabinet. The nearly full bottle of sherry was more than half gone.

Maybe getting some fresh air would help her headache. Anyway, she needed to get out of the house and away from Bella.

"I'm going to the grocery store. Would you like anything?"

"Some of those delicious cream-filled donuts."

Of course, Bella chose something she didn't need. I think she's gained at least five pounds this past week.

It was a gorgeous October day in Charleston. Hannah loved the colorful trees, but always thought fall was a depressing time. Although the wind was brisk, the sun felt wonderful. Hannah decided to walk the few blocks to the store. She bought the basics they were out of, along with a whole chicken to roast for dinner, some fresh green beans, and Bella's donuts.

As she left the store, Ben Garfield called to her from the ABC store across the street.

"Haven't seen much of you lately, Hannah, but Bella is a frequent customer. I thought you should know she's run up a substantial bill. She pays a little all along, but then increases her purchases."

"Oh, dear! Thanks for telling me, Ben. I'll have a talk with her."

Hannah's headache returned. When she reached home, Bella was stretched out on the couch asleep, drooling all over the cushion. A glass lay turned over on the coffee table. Hannah picked it up, sniffed—bourbon. She must have a hidden stash.

Hannah put away the groceries and checked the cabinet. Only a bit of the sherry remained. She took more aspirin and went to lie down. Bella hadn't touched her side of the room or the bathroom. *I don't know how much more of this I can stand.* As her headache eased, she drifted off to sleep.

The next day, Hannah got up at her usual time. Bella lay snoring, huffing and puffing like the wolf in *The Three Little Pigs*. She found that Bella hadn't cleaned up her mess from yesterday and had added to it last night—clothing and wet towels strewn everywhere. Hannah washed her face, brushed her teeth, and got out of the bathroom as fast as possible, dressed, and went into the kitchen. Bella's supper dishes were still on the table. The empty sherry bottle stood on the counter. Peering into the kitchen garbage can, she found the bourbon bottle. Bella was out of booze unless she had some hidden.

Sighing, Hannah fixed a breakfast of bacon, eggs, and toast. Hungry from the scant supper she'd had last night, she devoured every bite, washed her dishes, wiped the countertops, and left Bella's mess on the table. In an attempt to brighten her mood, she put on her gardening shoes and went out into the garden. It was a beautiful morning with the chrysanthemums displaying their colors. Hannah tugged on her gloves and began setting out bulbs. She felt better already. She loved gardening and lost track of time. A twinge in her back caused her to straighten up and stretch.

"Oh, there you are. I'm going into town. Those donuts weren't fit to eat this morning. I had to do with a couple pieces of toast. I'll have a late lunch in my favorite café." Bella climbed into their old Ford and clattered down the driveway.

Hannah knew her main stop would be the ABC store. At least she had dressed decently, although garishly, in a purple polyester pants suit with a red shawl thrown over her shoulders. Her back still aching, Hannah looked at her watch. It was already noon. She picked a bunch of chrysanthemums and went inside, hoping Bella had cleaned off the table. She hadn't, just added to the mess. Hannah felt like picking up the tablecloth and ditching everything. She let her anger cool and placed the dirty dishes in the sink. No way would she wash them. Putting the chrysanthemums in a blue vase, Hannah placed them on the table, and put on a can of soup. While it heated, she checked the household money—gone, every penny.

Hannah dropped down at the table, placed her head on her arms, and wept. The smell of scorched soup brought her to her feet. She burned her hand as she grabbed the pot and threw it into the sink. What were they going to do? They still had two weeks before they received their household allowance. Papa had been very strict with their trust—delegating money for every conceivable need. Perhaps he'd known of Bella's drinking problem. She'd have to dip into the savings from her personal allowances to tide them over. But this was the last straw. When the new allowance came, she'd take her half and leave. Let Bella manage the best way she could.

Bella came in and thrust a package of donuts in Hannah's face.

"See, baked today—fresh!"

"Bella, we've got to talk. Come into the living room." She heard the clink of glass in Bella's tote bag—her booze. "Sit down."

"What's so important? My trip tired me out. I need to go lie down."

And have a nip, Hannah thought. "The household money is gone. What do you propose we do for the next two weeks?"

"Oh, that! I knew you had some savings from your personal allowances. We can use that, and I'll pay you back out of my share. Such a fuss about nothing."

Bella flounced into their bedroom and slammed the door.

Hannah knew she'd never be reimbursed. For the next two weeks, she kept her cool as Bella's drinking grew worse, and the house looked like a pigsty. On the first of the month, she drove to Papa's attorney's office.

"Hi, Hannah. Come for your monthly allowances?"

"Yes, and Mr. Bradford, I have a favor to ask."

"I'll help if I can."

"I'm moving out of the house for a while. I need to get away. I would like to pick up my half of the allowances and leave the remainder for Bella to get. I'm leaving her the car."

"No problem. My services are available if you need them."

"Thanks, Mr. Bradford. Do you happen to know of a nice room I could rent?"

"As a matter of fact, I do. My wife's friend runs a boarding house." He wrote the landlady's name, address, and phone number on a pad and gave it to her. "I believe she can fix you up"

"Thanks again. I'll see you next month."

Hannah had packed her things and stowed them in the car while Bella slept.

She drove to the address she'd been given. The house was a large colonial in a nice neighborhood. A well-dressed lady answered the bell.

"Come in, dear. You must be Miss Sprague. Mr. Bradford called saying you needed a room. I have just the thing, a recent vacancy."

Hannah was thrilled with the room. It was large and tastefully decorated with a private bath and a closet-sized kitchenette. "It's lovely, but I'm not sure I can afford it."

"We'll work something out. You're just the kind of tenant I'm looking for. The last gentleman smoked like a chimney. You don't smoke, do you?"

"Goodness, no."

Mrs. Landsford named a figure. "Is that within your budget?"

"Oh, yes," Hannah said, reaching into her purse.

"I collect monthly. Will that suit?"

"Perfect. I have my belongings in the car. I'll bring them up, then I need to run some errands."

After depositing her things in her room, Hannah went to the grocery store. She'd have to be thrifty, but without Bella's booze and endless sweets, she should be fine.

Returning, she put away the groceries in her tiny kitchen with its apartment-sized appliances. Now the hard part—telling Bella.

* * *

Bella greeted her with, "Where have you been all this time? I thought I'd have to send out a search party. I need my allowance."

"I'm moving out, Bella. I already have a place. I'll leave you the car."

Bella's mouth fell open. "W-What do you mean? What will happen to me?"

"I can't stand living with you any longer. You expect me to do all the work. I refuse to put up with your drinking and clean up after you. I suggest you go to AA, get your drinking under control, and learn to take care of yourself. Mr. Bradford will have your share of the allowance on the first of the month. Goodbye, Bella."

"You can't just walk off. You'll get lonely, run out of money, and be back here. I give you a couple of months. Maybe I won't welcome you," Bella screeched.

Hannah called a taxi and left. The first two weeks were delightful. She loved the quiet, made trips to the library, and read to her heart's content. She cooked only the dishes she liked and kept her apartment spotless.

The other renters were middleaged men with day jobs so Hannah rarely saw them. Occasionally, Mrs. Landsford would invite her for mid-morning tea. She enjoyed their chats. If her budget permitted near the end of the month, she dined out and went to a movie.

She had to admit that she sometimes felt lonely and remembered the good times the sisters had before Bella began to drink heavily. They played her favorite game, Scrabble, and Bella's choice, Rummy. They ate out, went to the movies, and shopped together. She missed these times, but not the situation she'd left behind.

Hannah wondered how Bella was getting along. She'd given Bella her address and telephone number and told her to call in case of an emergency. Bella hadn't called.

Hannah had been on her own for a month now, and it was time to pick up her half of the allowance.

Mr. Bradford greeted her with a smile. "You just missed Bella. She asked if you'd been in yet."

"How did Bella seem?"

"Now that you ask, I believe she's lost a few pounds. Her manner and clothes were more subdued."

"That's good. She seems to be coping."

"I hope you girls will work out your differences." Mr. Bradford raked a trembling hand through his thinning hair.

He must be in his eighties, Hannah thought, amused that he'd called them girls. She took a taxi because it was raining. Walking made her short of breath lately.

The next day the weather cleared. Hannah walked to the store and planned to get a taxi back. An unexpected cloudburst hit before she got half way there, soaking her to the skin. Beginning to shiver, she hurried with her shopping and called a taxi. She trudged up the stairs and dumped the grocery bag on the table, stripped off her wet clothes, and took a hot shower. Dressed in her warmest robe, she heated a can of chicken soup.

By night, Hannah began to sneeze, so she ate more soup and went to bed. The next morning, she had a mild sore throat and her forehead felt warm. She swallowed a couple of aspirin and ate a bowl of cream of wheat, planning to take it easy today and read. Soon, she began to have chills, crawled into bed, pulling the covers to her chin. Hannah awoke alternately burning up and freezing, but managed to get up and go to the bathroom. Plagued with frequent colds, she kept a stock of over-the-counter cold remedies. She took a spoonful of medicine, which promised to eliminate all symptoms.

Hannah made a bowl of cream of wheat, adding milk to make it easier to swallow. Her throat felt as if flames were coursing up and down and out even to her ears. Before returning to bed, Hannah popped a throat lozenge in her mouth. She slept until a fit of coughing awoke her. Fortunately, she had cough syrup, which allowed her to go back to sleep.

Hannah slept until five o'clock and went on wobbly legs to drink a cup of soup, go to the bathroom, and take more of her remedies. She wasn't sleepy, but didn't feel like sitting up. *I wish Bella were here.* Her sister, in her sober moments, had always taken care of her when she was ill. Hannah crawled back into bed feeling sorry for herself. The night brought a high fever, night sweats, chills, and nightmares.

The next morning, Hannah awoke to a tapping on her door.

"Hannah, dear, are you all right? I've missed seeing you. May I come in?"

Hannah struggled to open the door and almost fainted in Mrs. Landsford's arms.

"Oh, my dear, I'm so sorry you're ill. Come, I'll help you back to bed." Mrs. Landsford touched her forehead. "Goodness, child. You're burning up. You must see a doctor."

"No, I often have colds and bronchitis," Hannah managed to say, her voice harsh and raspy.

"I'm afraid this is more than just a cold. I'll call my physician. He's a friend and I think I can persuade him to come by. You don't need to go out in this rain. I'll be back in a minute." Mrs. Landsford returned saying, "He'll be here at noon. The dear is taking his lunch hour. Now I'm going to make us some tea. It will help your shivering."

Dr. Crosby arrived on time, examined Hannah, and gave her antibiotics.

"You have a bad case of bronchitis. When we clear up this infection, I want you to come into my office for some tests. You shouldn't get colds and bronchitis as often as you do."

Hannah agreed, thanked him for coming out, and paid him.

She felt miserable the next week with fits of coughing waking her up. The simplest task made her short of breath. She lost her appetite, and as a result, several pounds. She suffered from pain in her chest and back, and extreme weakness kept her in bed.

Mrs. Landsford became her self-appointed nurse. She administrated her medicine and coaxed her to eat and drink liquids. Hannah felt like she sloshed when she walked to the bathroom.

Her landlady made her an appointment with Dr. Crosby for the end of next week. Hannah hoped she would be up to it. The day of the appointment, Hannah dragged herself to the bathroom. Looking in the mirror, she hardly recognized herself. She was pale with bruises under her sunken eyes. She shuddered. Her mama would say she looked like death warmed over.

Mrs. Landsford drove her to the doctor's office. He bombarded her with questions about her medical history, frowning at her answers.

He gave her a chest x-ray.

Hannah couldn't be still, twisting her hands together while waiting on the results.

She shook with fear when Dr. Crosby came back into the room.

"I'm sorry, but the x-ray showed several masses on both of your lungs. I'll schedule an MRI for a clearer picture. We must do a biopsy."

"Oh, no!"

"We'll insert a needle and collect a small amount of tissue. Don't worry, now. The tumors might be benign. The nurse will prepare you."

The actual biopsy wasn't too bad. Hannah lay almost in a fetal position on the examining table. *Not worry? The doctor is crazy.*

She was to have the MRI tomorrow. Dr. Crosby assured her he'd call as soon as he had the results. He told her to rest. Hannah was as jumpy as a jack-in-the-box, waiting on the doctor's call. When he did and Mrs. Landsford made her an appointment, she sat on her bed, hugging herself and rocking back and forth. Thankfully, she was seeing the doctor the next morning and managed to pull herself together. Always a stoic, she'd accept whatever the verdict was.

As soon as she saw the doctor's face, she knew it was bad news.

"Hannah, I'm sorry. It's cancer—an aggressive form. It has spread to your liver and lymph nodes. Surgery is not an option. We'll start you on chemotherapy."

"How long do I have, Dr. Crosby?"

"It's hard to say. The treatments may slow it down some. Maybe as long as three months."

"And without the chemotherapy?"

"A few weeks to a month."

"I don't want the treatments. I hear they're as bad as the disease."

"It's your choice. There are side effects. The pain you've been experiencing will grow worse. I'll give you some strong painkillers and at the end, morphine. I'm so sorry."

Holding in her despair and holding back her tears, Hannah rose and met Mrs. Landsford in the waiting room. When they got in the car, Mrs. Landsford asked, "Was it good news, dear?"

"I have terminal cancer. Maybe a month to live. I'm going home to die."

"Oh, my dear, I'm so sorry. You've become a good friend." She wiped tears from her face.

Once in her room, Hannah sank down on her bed and let the tears come. She sobbed until there were no tears left, washed her face, and packed her belongings. She struggled downstairs with her things and called a taxi.

Mrs. Landsford came out of her room. "Oh, I wanted to take you home."

"It's better this way."

"I'll come visit and you let me know if there is anything I can do to make things easier for you."

"I will. Thank you so much for your kindness." Hannah hugged her just as the taxi pulled up.

During the drive, Hannah wondered how Bella was and if she would welcome her. The taxi driver brought her suitcases to the porch. Hannah paid him, straightened her back, and walked in.

The house was neat and Bella was dressed. She had lost weight.

"So you decided to come home. Did you run out of money?"

"No, I came home because I'm dying."

Bella swallowed, opened and closed her mouth like a fish with no sound coming out.

Hannah marched into Papa's bedroom. With its dark furnishings, it would be a fitting place to die. A wry smile curved her mouth. Finally, she'd had the last word.

You Are the Boy With the Sunlit Hair
By Kathryn Jeffcoat

You are the boy with the sunlit hair, playing in the tall grass.
You are all the tender moments perpetually unfolding.
You and I have known a thousand waves surging,
and the waiting so long, so tremulously
for the static dizziness a kiss could be,
we have whispered the dreams of our growing souls
and learned that love could be worse than a catastrophe;
And there is more, so much more, you and I are, and have been than this,
you and I know, and have learned than this.
You are the boy in the tall grass,
you are the whisper that calms my fear,
 I am your delinquent angel, and the warmth that you pull near.

You are always to me
the boy with the sunlit hair,
playing in the tall grass,
on long golden afternoons.
and also the long-awaited, broad-shouldered, shadow at the door
the heavy and tired, footsteps coming across the floor
the embraces where the world melts away
the truth of love and more than this
the deafening quaking of my heart
in the foolish moment I may half turn away
in anger, in madness, in darkness, in despair
you are still the boy in the tall grass with the sunlit hair
and I cannot turn away
I so quickly lose the will
I twist, I cry, I fall, I love you still.
Now, maybe you wonder what the point is
in saying all of this
It is just to tell you I am here, and not to fret
we haven't quite driven each other crazy yet
and one day when you are kissing me
I will forget.

In the Garden
By Dick Brook

God has this Garden called Eden and Adam and Eve are the caretakers, and there's this one tree that bears such tasty fruit that only God is allowed to eat of it. It makes him smart, and powerful, and sometimes quite gassy. Adam harvests all the fruits of the garden and makes sure that the ones from the forbidden tree get into God's basket alone.

"I'm pleased," says God. "You do this very well, Adam."

"Thank you."

"This is all there is today? Just what's here in My basket?"

"Of course. I haven't learned to steal yet. Eve will apparently teach me, but right now I'm ignorant of the knowledge of good and evil."

"Hey, that doesn't mean you can't sin. It just says if you do, you won't know it. In fact, what this apple here will do for you"—God lifts a scarlet fruit from His own basket—"is help you sort things out. You eat this and you'll know when you're sinning. Even the first bite will tell you it's stolen. Otherwise, the ethical significance of life's events would be lost on you."

Adam frowns.

"Are you sure you're God?" he says.

"It's My garden."

"What if you're the devil?"

"What if you are?" God smirks.

"I asked you first."

"OK. Let's say I'm the devil. Would I show up like this in a flowing beard, long white toga, surrounded by a cloud of cherubs?"

All at once, little babies with wings crowd around a suspended microphone and sing, "Stand by Me." Adam listens for a minute, tapping his toe, and when they finish, he turns to God and speaks.

"You're asking me," says Adam, "if a show like this is heartfelt?"

"Right. I'd look like a snake in the grass, wouldn't I, if I trotted out these kids and had them puff up my false perfection?" God opens both his hands and—palms up—shows he does not carry a weapon.

"I'm a little naïve yet," Adam says, "but I suppose God would not want to make that kind of bad impression."

"Right," God says. "So if I were the devil, you'd know me right off. That's one of the rules of the game."

"Making it easy to tell who the devil is," says Adam, "could defeat the whole purpose of the test, couldn't it?"

"What test?" says God.

"I have the feeling you don't trust me."

"Really? You think my looking like God, though I might be the very devil, would undermine the virtue of the Lord?"

"Yes," says Adam. "Even if I were first of all naïve, and if second I occupied the devil's office, I'd show up looking like God."

"And if you were God?"

"That's moot. I wouldn't have to show up at all. I'd already be here."

"That's good. I like that. But in the form of a snake?"

"Yes, maybe. To make the test convincing."

"Which means," says God, "you're gonna listen to the snake rather than a guy in a long white beard?"

"Eve," Adam calls into the grove. "Can you come here a minute?"

"I was picking fruit," says Eve.

"You do it perfectly," says the guy who looks like God.

"Thank you," Eve says. "Adam taught me. He was here first."

"Not really," says the guy who still looks like God. "But that's another story."

"What's up?" says Eve.

"God and I," Adam says, "are discussing the devil."

"Yes," says God. "It's a friendly discussion about identities."

"Then again, maybe this white guy is the devil," says Adam *sotto voce*.

"Who are we talking about?" says Eve looking around. "I'm as naïve as the next guy."

"This Fellow with the beard," says Adam, "is presumably divine."

"Then again," says Eve, "he could be the very devil himself. Like in Elmer Gantry."

"That hasn't been written yet," says the Person in the white beard.

"I find it strange," Eve says, "that time—the before and the after—should be a problem for you."

"Exactly," says Adam. "Just who's who around here?"

"I'm God," says the Person in the toga. "Let the devil speak for himself."

Embarrassed silence.

"Is there a reason why I don't hear anything?" says Eve.

"It's a long hike," says God, rolling his eyes. "And punctuality was never his virtue. Give him a minute."

"You rang?" says a long oily snake in the Big Tree.

"Yuck," says Eve. "This is the snake?"

"This is the devil," says the one believed to be God.

"The purported devil," says Adam.

"No," says the snake. "This is no joke. I am indeed the devil himself!" The snake droops down from his limb, and with a few slurps, quickly sticks out his tongue.

"I hadn't bargained for this," Eve says with a shudder. "I have work to do, getting and spending." She waits a moment, glaring at the snake. "I'm not here to hang about doing silly business with boys." Eve steps under a sign marked EXIT and pauses.

"That's a woman's wit," says the snake, apparently peeved. "Move on then, shrew. I'll strike a deal with Adam."

"That's my girl," says God. "Reject him."

"I'm not your girl. I'm not anybody's 'girl.'"

Eve departs. There is an awkward silence.

"That was a flop," says the snake with an embarrassed, eye-to-eye grin, and dangles himself from his limb.

"What was a flop?" Adam tips his head sideways to better[1] see the vertical snake, from end to end.

"God here made plans for Eve and me," says the serpent.

"You can't make plans with a woman," the one who looks like God says. "You can't even get a hearing. I often send angels."

"Look," says Adam. "What's the point here? Who called this meeting?"

"I did," say both the snake and God at the same time.

"You first," Adam says to God.

"Yes," says God. "Adam, I wanted to tell you how much I've appreciated your work here in the garden."

The young man bends his eyebrows as if he's ready to be disappointed.

But God goes on. "You're the tops when it comes to planting and picking."

"Get the technique," says the snake as if to the pit. "Straight from the Handbook." He sticks out his tongue, slurps, and points his tail at the cluttered condition of the Garden with its unraked leaves, seedy rose hips, and clutter of fallen branches. "And I'm the father of lies?"

Adam wrinkles his nose and nods at the snake while thanking the Deity.

"But," says God.

"Here it comes," says the snake.

"Here it comes," says Adam, a sudden victim of *paradisiacal echolalia*.

"I think," says God, implying there are times when he doesn't, "you'll be much happier someplace else."

"Huh?" says Adam.

"Hee hee," says the snake, slapping his knee.

"I'm building a parking lot," says God with a rumble. "The garden goes." He says to Adam, "You, you're on the street."

"I can't believe this," says Adam and he covers his ears.

"You didn't hear it from the snake," says the snake. He pried one hand loose from Adam's head. "Now who's your buddy?"

"Can we talk?" says Adam to God.

"Sorry. This meeting is over," God says.

"So much for solidarity," Adam says to no one in particular.

"A few notes for the record," says God, preparing to walk off into the clouds. "The garden will be leveled and blacktopped. You and Eve will have moved on. I would have sent Michael to explain all this, but it's his turn on the dozer." The growing roar of a diesel engine can be heard in the distance. "He's scraping away the fields of maize and millet this very instant."

On the near horizon, a young man with blond hair and wide wings stands up at the wheel of an orange tractor and waves his cowboy hat.

"Hi, everybody," says the young man, "I'm scraping away the fields of maize and millet." He sits down on a springy seat and drives off with a tangle of pear trees and raspberry bushes on the shield of his bulldozer.

"Can't we talk about this?" says Adam.

"Don't be second-guessing me," says God. "The deal's sealed. I've spent the advance."

----

[1] The Snake often splits his infinitives for emphasis.

"You're hisstory," says the snake to Adam with a narrow grin.

"It's true. You're downsized, baby" says God, looking soberly into Adam's face.

"This is the thanks I get? Not a pat on the back?"

"You can use my cell phone for one week," says God.

"Thanks for nothing," says Adam. "But I will take a few apples for Eve." He plucks two from the Big Tree. "How will I explain this to her?"

"Tell her it was her fault," says the snake, "for leaving the audience."

"All of you," God says, waving his staff with a new impatience, "Out of here!"

"Make way for Walmart," shouts the snake with a snicker.

"Where are you parked?" says Adam, putting his hand on the snake's shoulder as they walk away.

"At the end of the asphalt. I brought the hearse."

"We'll be back," Adam says and turns to shake his fist in the air.

"Never is too soon," says the Deity with a jaunty laugh.

And it came to pass that Adam talked Eve into listening to his snake. The Bible has it backward. And from then on Adam earns his bread by sweat. This much is true. His children grow up to figure in murders and statistics on recidivism. God Himself is downsized in the 19th Century, though he fights back until the middle of the 20th. The snake goes to work for the phone company in 1971. And Eve? It turns out Eve is divine.

"I knew it all along," she says, while blowing on her nails with a saucy pucker.

Christmas Gift
By Elsie Holcombe

He had stopped trying to pick out a Christmas gift for her. She just didn't seem to like the food processor with all the attachments he had bought her. She had taken back the coat he picked out for her one year, and the time he gave her the Coleman camping stove to use at the lake, well, for some strange reason, she had seemed downright angry.

George just didn't understand why. She knew he had been talking about how much easier it would be for them to have a gas stove. It meant faster cooking for her and less trouble for him than having to build a fire on the outdoor grill each time they went to the lake. And she had *really* fouled up that year when he gave her a fishing rod (just her size) so she could learn to enjoy fishing with him. After that, he just started giving her a nice check or putting some money in an envelope so she could get what she wanted.

"It's just too heavy to get that big thing down from the cabinet and I have too much to wash up if I try to use all those things that go with it," she had explained when he asked why she didn't use the food processor.

What Marge didn't say was that she hated it. Why couldn't he give her something like a frilly nightie or a lovely piece of expensive jewelry? She knew they couldn't afford it, but why did he always have to pay cash for everything; and why, if he had to pay cash, didn't he at least get something personal for her? A camp stove and a fishing rod? Her blood pressure went sky-high every time she thought about them. He seemed hurt that she didn't use the fishing rod. After

all, they both liked being around water, and their horoscopes were both water signs. He was a Pisces and she was the Crab. "How true," he always joked.

She had really appreciated the coat even though it was sizes too large for her. She was only five feet tall; the sleeves had hung down three inches beyond her hands and the hem puddled onto the floor. There was nothing else to do but exchange it. The problem was she had to choose another style.

***

The next year, she got some money in an envelope. When she said she really would have liked a little gift, he said, "Well, last year, you took back the coat you didn't like, so I thought you would rather buy a present for yourself, something that you *would* like."

And so it went on for several years . . . another Christmas, another envelope. The children started putting big colorful bows on the envelopes.

Then one year, when she was in the midst of wrapping scores of presents, Marge said to her oldest daughter in a rather reproachful tone, "I wonder what color ribbon your Daddy would like for you to put on my envelope this year?"

That's when Ann said, "Look, Mom, instead of feeling miserable because Daddy doesn't know how to buy a gift, and you don't really want us to do it for him, why don't you just go out and buy yourself something that you really like, wrap it up, ask him to sign his name on the card and then open it up on Christmas morning?"

"Oh, I don't know about that. It just wouldn't be the same as having him buy me something and it would seem like such a sham."

"Well, OK, then would you rather have something like another camp stove or a fishing rod or just another envelope?"

That did it! The thought of the stove and fishing rod sent her blood pressure rising
again. "Let's go!"

The sweater was beautiful. It was electric blue in a nice knobby knit. It brought out the blue in her eyes and was just the right length.

"Oh, but Ann, look at the price," she said. "It's so expensive!" The sweater was a *Liz Claiborne* and had all of the fine details that made its name proud.

"Well, Mom, I don't know how much a fishing rod costs, but . . .'"

The sales clerk knew just the right moment to say, "You know all of the sweaters are forty percent off and with the coupon, that's another five dollars."

"I'll take it," Marge said, "and I want that pretty silk *Liz Claiborne* scarf to go with it; and have the person at the wrapping counter put it in a box and use the prettiest paper and biggest bow they have." She squared her shoulders, looked in Ann's direction, and said, "So there!"

***

George was sitting in his chair watching TV when she got home. Marge plopped the shiny gold package with the over-

sized red bow onto his lap and handed him a lovely card that read, "To My Wife at Christmastime." She pointed to the card and said, "Sign this."

"What is it?"

"It's your Christmas present to me. *Sign* the card."

"What's in it?" he asked as he dutifully wrote, "Love, George," on the spot she pointed
to. "It's a surprise from you to me and it can't be opened until Christmas."

"Well, don't you think I should know what I'm giving you?"

"Did you buy it?"

George grinned and muttered, "No, but . . ."

She took it out of his hand and put it under the tree. "Well, if you didn't buy it, you will have to wait and be surprised when I open it . . . just like I will be."

The package outshone all of the others under the tree. The whole family kept asking, "Whose is that?"

Marge just answered, "It is your Dad's Christmas present to me."

"What is it, Dad?"

He just shot a quizzical look at Marge, smiled, and answered, "We'll see."

When she opened the box on Christmas morning, all eyes were on her. The sweater was even more beautiful than she remembered. The scarf was a lovely blend of electric blue, green, and purple and matched perfectly. Even George viewed the opening with an unusual interest, and then sat back with an air of pride and accomplishment.

***

The next year, Marge started shopping for her gift a little earlier with a feeling of excitement and anticipation. She became even a little more daring and looked at some fine jewelry. There was just one problem. She fell in love.

The ring was a huge pearl the size of a pea. Pin-size diamonds stretched out from it on either side; but it was *$500.* She walked around the store and went back to look at it three times before she left.

The next three weeks took her back to the store several times. Each time she went she visited "her ring." The pearl was the birthstone for the month of June, and Marge's birthday was in June. When she tried it on, a feeling of belonging swept over her . . . the *zing* she always felt when she knew something was right for her. She even managed to show it to George and the kids once, but they showed little interest. The kids were shopping for gifts for their friends and George for a new hunting knife; he just muttered, "Hmmm, nice," before he took off in the direction of the sporting department. But she kept visiting *her* ring. It gave her a warm feeling of satisfaction.

Then one day it was gone. Her feelings were mixed, a sense of loss yet relief over something that "wasn't meant to be." She sighed and told herself that now she could stop thinking about it.

Marge half-heartedly shopped for another gift for herself; she needed new makeup so replaced a few small items, wrapped them in a very large box, and

went through the routine of having George sign his card again. She was even a little annoyed with him because he seemed to enjoy having his gift-giving become so easy. He didn't even ask what it was.

***

Christmas morning came, and once again, all eyes were upon her. She smiled and pretended to be exited when she opened the box she had wrapped. Inside was the makeup she had bought. But there was something else . . . the old familiar envelope. What had happened? She looked around in complete puzzlement.

"Well, open it, open it, what are you waiting for," one voice after another kept repeating.

She opened the envelope; out fell three $10 bills and . . . the RING!!!

"Oh, George, how?" she managed to whisper in a tear-choked voice. "But it's so *expensive.*"

"Quit worrying about the price. If it will make you feel any better, it was thirty percent off. Put it on and go buy yourself that nightgown you want. Just don't make it another flannel one." With that, he gave her a big wink.

"Yeah, Mom," teased one of the boys, "Get yourself a pretty sexy one." He thought he was being pretty funny and daring, and so did the other five kids. Their giggles were a little nervous, but Marge just shook her head, laughed too, and sought Dad's eyes. The look they shared was theirs alone.

***

She took Mary with her to buy the gown. Mary was only three and was quite a handful in the store. She swished in and out of the racks of lingerie and gowns, delighting in their soft silky smoothness. Suddenly, she pulled the edge of a negligee out from under the rainbow cloud of colors arched over her. It was a hot-pink filmy chiffon nightie covering a satin undergown. It looked like cotton candy swaying in her little hands.

"Mommy," she called out in her loud little shrill voice, "Is dis one sexy 'nough for
Daddy?"

Marge stood in stunned silence. The world stopped still. A sudden hush seemed to descend over the whole store. The saleslady put both hands to her mouth to keep the laughter that was rising in her from exploding.

But that wasn't all. "Mommy, what does *sexy* mean?"

Marge gasped, looked around, and felt the red flush travel slowly down her entire body. By then, several customers were in gales of laughter. The sales lady came to the rescue.

"It means 'pink,'" she said, "a pretty pink, just the color you have in your hand."

"Dat's what I thought," nodded little Mary knowingly. She looked up at her mother with a pleased expression. "It's sooo . . . pretty!"

"It is," soothed the clerk in as matter-of-fact tone as she could muster. "In fact, it's one of the loveliest we have in the store and on sale right now, too."

"I'll take it," Marge answered in a voice that was almost a whisper. She didn't ask the price.

"Do you want it wrapped?"

"No, no, just a bag. Thank you, thank you. Let's go, Mary."

Marge didn't take a deep breath until they got back home.

***

George was in his favorite chair, reading his paper. Mary ran to him, gave him an excited hug and pulled the guilty gown from the bag.

"Look, Daddy, look. Mommy bought a gown wit the money you gave her! It's sooo boootiful and it's sexy-color!"

George's eyebrows went up. He glanced at Marge with a look that said, "What's this?"

"Ask her," Marge said quietly with a flush of remembrance.

Mary danced around the room. "Isn't it boootiful? I picked it out by *myself*! I knew sexy meant 'pink' when everybody laughed at the store and the lady told me I was wight. Don't you think it's sexy-pink, too? I weally picked it out all by *myself*."

George threw back his head and roared, pulled Marge onto his lap, draped the filmy gown around her shoulders, his eyes sparkling, and choked, "Yes, I do. And I think Mommy should wear it with that 'boootiful' new pearl ring that Daddy picked out for her all by *himself* for Christmas."

The Naughty Lady of Shady Lane
By Janet Sheppard Kelleher

After we buried my husband, George, things went from bad to worse. I tried to make like things were well on the surface, but they weren't. Anyway, some high and mighty in town got wind of our problems and reported it to the gover-ment. And they sent out a woman to—what they call—*assess* the sitiation. They was gonna try to prove I couldn't support the younguns and put them in a orphanage, I just knowed it!

Right from the git-go I knowed this weren't gonna turn out good. I'll tell ya for why . . . 'cause when that old witch got there, I recognized her. I did, I knowed her when I was agrowing up. She use to live right here in Gopher Hill and prostituted her body to the men who'd pay for it. Yes, sir-ree, and she was standing right there on my doorstep, the dad-blamed tramp! She still looked like she been rode hard and put away wet, if you'll pardon my pun.

I said, "Jezebel, what you doing here? I'm expecting a lady from the gover-ment."

She said, "I *am* the lady from the government!"

I told her, "Go tell it to a sailor on horseback. You *ain't* no lady. Never have been. You got the gall to show your face around here after what I done to you last time I laid eyes on you?"

"Look here, Julia, you needn't be too uppity. You got a past, too, you know!"

"Yeah, I do, but I certainly didn't need no penicillin to get over mine! Listen here, you old mule in horse harness, I want you off'n my land."

"Well, lady, I hate to tell you, but the fact is you're just sharecropping here. This ain't your land to order me around on. You can't even call your soul your own. I just need to come in and ask you a few questions, that's all."

"My *soul* belongs to the Lord, you tainted woman—which is more than I can say for you!"

I wondered what did she need to know? And what'd happen if I didn't tell the truth? I decided I wasn't about to let somebody take my chi'ren away. The Lord would just have to understand that what I did . . . I had to do.

I told her to wait just a minute. I went and got granddaddy's old shotgun. When I got back to the screen door, I cocked the thing, looked down the barrel, and I says to her, "I ain't dealing with no home-wrecking hussy from my past. You tell those collar-and-tie men at the agency I said that, you hear?"

I studied on that thing, and decided I was not letting Jezebel in my house. That slut done give more than her share a men the clap and she didn't care whose marriage she sent through wrack and ruination. Why, she'd put more people through torment 'cause of her *perfession* than anybody I knowed. And here she was, continuing to spread suffering like the bubonic plague. By Godfrey, I stopped her in her tracks that day, though.

Well, I got my son, Ed, to check on the sitiation for me. He said she really did work with the gover-ment, and I hadn't ought to pull the gun on the woman like I did. Well, I just couldn't help myself. You see, when we was young, we got into a knock-down-drag-out. I seen her stop David out in front of the hardware store one day. He was betrothed to my best friend, Sarah, at the time. David was a real good man and wouldn't flirt with any woman—let alone Jezebel.

You know she cut her eyes at me to make sure I was watching and reached up and kissed him, *on the lips*, mind you. Just like waving it in my face that she could take any man she wanted. And when I seen David back off from her, spit, and wipe his mouth with the back of his hand, I knowed he weren't guilty a no wrongdoing.

Well, I weren't gonna put up with her kissing my best friend's fella, no sir-ree. I dropped my sack a nails and run over there. I punched her in the eye so hard, she got off balance in them spike heels a hers and fell to the ground. Now David didn't see me coming, 'cause his back was turned to me. So the look a surprise on his face was beyond words!

I seen my chance right then and there to even the score for a whole heap a women—and I taken it! I jumped on top of her as hot as the seven brass hinges a Hell, and I intended to get shed a that hustler once and for all! I pounded her for all I was worth.

After a mite, David tried to pull me off of her, but I hit him, too. By then, a little crowd done gathered and was cheering me on! They all knowed her 'cause she was always lurking around somewheres in town seducing bidness. So right there in front a God and everybody, I beat that woman 'til you couldn't recognize her.

Some folks told me later that they run over to get the sheriff, but when they explained what was going on, he was slow as wet gunpowder getting there. He told me later he thought I could do more in 10 minutes than he did in the last 10 years. And ya know what? That sheriff was right! I run that brazen floozy outta Gopher Hill. Nobody seen her again that I recollect 'til she showed up at my door that day, looking all highfalutin.

People say that's why your Aunt Fannie's so feisty. You see, I was pregnant with her at the time I knocked that woman cat-west.

When Sarah got wind of the woman being here, she come to have a heart-to-heart talk with me. "Was it *really* that old Jezebel that went to your house?" she asked me. "It's been more than twenty years; how could you possibly recognize her?"

I said, "Yes, Sarah, it were that old witch I beat up all them years ago. When you rearrange somebody's face like I did hers, you don't soon forget the look in their eyes! It was there. And she had her tail up and stinger out, ready for action. Revenge had to be the first thing on her mind."

"Well, Julia, I won't let them take your chi'ren. I just won't let that happen to you. I'll figure something out."

And I knowed she would. She's a smart woman.

At church the next Sunday morning, the preacher announced that one of the flock was in need. He ask us to sign up in the vestibule what we could give. God knows I sure ain't had no money, but I wrote down I could maybe give a few eggs or a chicken once't in a while. I didn't know they was atalking about me.

Sarah done told every member. She thought if they got the preacher to write a letter saying they was bound to give us a certain amount a money and stuff every week, the agency'd let me keep the chi'ren.

A friend at church knowed someone who worked at that agency, and she told me when that rat was acoming back. Old Jezebel showed up again with a man from the gover-ment, but I was ready for them this time. I had a apple cobbler in the oven, smelling like we was eating high on the hog every day. I invited them in like they come to do me a favor, and offered some cobbler and coffee. I figured if I was nice this time, the man might think Jezebel'd lied 'bout my holding that gun on her. Anyway, it were her word against mine. And who was people gonna believe, a old hooker or a Sunday-school teacher?

The man asked questions from an important-looking form. I answered truthfully. When he was done with his probing and closed his notebook, he had a sorry, pitiful look on his face. But the look on Jezebel's face was like she knowed she was gonna make me eat crow—she were convinced she was about to bring my saddle home. And, ooh, it looked like it pleased her to no end. Well, what happened next is the stuff dreams is made of.

Jezebel butted in just as the man was about to speak, "Sorry, Mrs. Lester. Looks like you don't have the funds to support your family. Gather the kids up, they're going with us."

I couldn't believe how cruel-hearted she was that she could just blurt out something like that. She'd dug up her tommyhawk and was ready for battle. 'Course, she musta done forgot who she was atalking to!

Now this part's slicker'n calves' slobber. Acting like I was ignoring her altogether, I looked at the man and said, "You'll want to see this letter from our church. It'll clear up this misunderstanding." I was just holding out to see how far they'd go.

Jezebel jerked it out'n the man's hand and read it aloud:

January 15, 1940

To Whom It May Concern:

    Please be informed that the Gopher Hill Church of Christ has set aside $3.50 each week for the Lester family. In addition, the Sheppards are providing the Lesters with their groceries at wholesale cost. The Porters are providing shoes and clothing at cost. The Matthews have promised to help with emergencies that might arise until the children are grown.

    With the money that Ed is making and the food they grow on the farm, this should sustain them without the government's assistance.

    If this declaration of intent is not sufficient to meet your requirements, we will make the necessary adjustments.

Sincerely Yours,
C.G. Boyd, Minister

I wish you coulda seen the look a defeat in Jezebel's eyes. Ohh, it was *priceless*! She had eight acres of hell in her and couldn't give it to nobody. She thought she done had me over a barrel, but I told her as I walked her to the door, "If the Lord be for us, who can be against us?"

Yes, sir; we'd reached the well at wit's end and Sarah saved my hide in the nick a time, and I didn't even ask for her help. She just saw the need and filled it. That's what friends do.

Last Mother
By Nan Lundeen

Valley of Fire, Nevada

Anasazi Mother,

at home among
prickly pear
sagebrush
lizard

did you sing to Moon?

Anasazi Mother,

boulder jumble
sandy canyon
coyote yip
burr of wasp

did snake speak to you?

Anasazi Mother,

spires spearing dry sky
pockmarked rock
cruel sun
red rock nest

did you dream of cool caves?

Anasazi Mother,

some say when a new shaman's hand
rests in a petroglyph handprint,
the shamans gone before
fill her with their spirits

what rock-locked wisdom do we need?

Anasazi Mother,

what knowledge lies buried
with your ancestors
under your kitchen floor?

Anasazi Mother,

when your hands failed
did you still yearn
to imprint sun-seared boulders?

when your lips burned
and your tongue swelled
did you keen at the water hole?

when your hearing failed
did you mourn
buzz of bee, wind stirring ricegrass?

when your heart failed
did you still struggle to ask Moon
why the rains no longer blessed the land
and all your children died?

+++

Eulogy
By Trilby Plants

Deep in November, the beach people and golfers have left the Grand Strand. I am alone on the causeway bridge—my favored spot to catch the elusive, delectable blue crab. It was cloudy and cold earlier when I left home, but the clouds have blown away, and the setting sun warms me.

Again I drop my baited basket into the creek. A few gulls swoop down and snatch up whatever floats on the current of the incoming tide.

After another hour, as my father would say, I have "nary a nibble."

My father was a bomber pilot during World War II. When I was eight years old, he left the Air Force and took advantage of the G.I. Bill. He went to graduate school at the University of Montana and earned two master's degrees: one in education and one in English.

Dad became a school superintendent, and we moved several times to small Montana towns until I was 16. As a teenager, I wasn't keen on pulling up roots so often, but Dad loved the prairies and the badlands.

I shined jackrabbits with him for a small cut of the bounty paid by the Department of Natural Resources—one way to preserve what little grass there was for cattle ranchers. Dad took me hunting with him, always seeking the mythical 10-point mule deer. We both loved venison.

Dad became an avid and talented lapidarist. He sliced agates, jasper, aventurine, and petrified wood on a homemade diamond saw, shaped the slabs, and crafted them into beautiful jewelry. From him I learned how to hunt agates. He drove his aging Packard into the Missouri breaks using cow paths for roads. In sun-baked gulches—always wary of rattlesnakes—I learned to see beyond the rough stone to the colors and the lace and moss of incursions in the translucent quartz. He showed me petrified wood with fossilized rings that measured a 100 million years of frozen time.

We camped, he and I, under curtains of Aurora Borealis: whorls of jasper, aventurine, tiger eye, and carnelian, that fluttered in some capricious solar wind. By the time I was 10, I could spot a good agate on the prairie 20 yards away.

He never made a concerted effort to market his creations, but gave them away as gifts and infrequently sold something if someone pressed him. I love the ones he gave me. Each one has a history—some I remember because I was part of the stone's transformation from lump of nondescript rock to semiprecious gemstone.

Of all my father's accomplishments, he prided himself most on being a great fisherman. When I was younger, he handed me the little brook trout he caught and showed me how to stretch them slightly to make sure they were the minimum six inches. We fried them and ate them bones and all for breakfast. When I was older, he often took me fishing with him. He tried to pass on his knowledge to me, but, as a fisherman, I was hopeless. I would have the same gear, same bait, and try to use the same technique. I would get nothing, nary a nibble, while Dad reeled in fish after fish.

If he were here on the bridge with me, he would be catching crabs. He would comment about crabbing and life in general. But he died 10 years ago, so I can't ask his advice.

I lean my elbows on the railing and watch a solitary kingfisher fish the evening, barely making a sound when he dives in the water. He flies up and perches on a stanchion in the channel where he gulps down a minnow. Down the creek, a great blue heron stands knee-deep in the water, almost blending into the lengthening shadows. A cormorant surfaces near the grassy edge of the creek, climbs onto a dry patch, and stretches her wings out to dry them.

My drifting mind comes back to blue crabs. I pull up my basket. Nothing. Maybe the crabs have gotten smart, and I'm wasting my time. But, unwilling to give up while there is still daylight, I drop the basket into the water again.

My father would like this marsh, even though it's a long way from the Western prairies and badlands. He would like the rhythms of the tides and the birds. He would enjoy fishing the creek, and he would take great pleasure in the pursuit of crabs.

I look to my right, and there he is, elbows on the railing. I can feel him in the evening silence of the marsh. He is wearing his usual plaid shirt, his glasses tucked in the pocket.

He grins and says, "Ah, Twiggles." It is the pet name nobody else has ever called me. "You're just not doing it right. You have to call them."

I remember he was very still while he fished. He would sit or stand, barely moving for long minutes, and then softly call, "Here, fishy fishy fishy." And they would come to him.

What do I have to lose? There is nobody around to see me. I lean over the railing and call, "Here, crabby crabby crabby." My voice floats out over the water.

I pull the string on the basket taut. I think I feel the metallic vibration of pincers transmitted up the string. Quickly, I pull in the line. It seems too weighty for a crab. Maybe I've picked up something off the bottom. The basket breaks the water's surface. A single crab clings to the chicken back—the biggest crab I've ever seen. My mind gleefully plans how to show off my trophy. In my excitement, the basket tilts. The crab scuttles over the edge and vanishes in the murky water.

"Oh, well," Dad says. "There are plenty more. And you have the story of the big one that got away."

He had many stories about big ones that had gotten away. And some trophies of ones that didn't.

I drop the basket again and call, "Here, crabby crabby crabby."

This time, I wait several minutes, forcing myself into stillness. Then I hold my breath, yank the basket up . . . and Voila! I have it. I can tell as soon as I scoop it up that it's big enough. My ruler measures it six inches from point to point—one inch over the minimum. I dump the crab in my bucket, careful not to get pinched.

"Gotcha," I gloat, while admiring its blue-tinged claws, open and raised in futile defiance. Another ounce of blue crab meat to add to my stash in the freezer. Already I'm deciding what to make: crab cakes or soup.

I throw my basket out again and call them. "Here, crabby crabby crabby."

I reel in another. Each time I drop the basket, I get a keeper or two.

After netting six more crabs, I look at Dad. He winks at me and says, "See. That's how it's done."

I remember learning to fly-fish. Dad deftly flicked his rod two o'clock and ten o'clock, two and ten, catching one brookie after another. I would always end up in an impossible snarl of line and gooseberry bushes. Picking the ber-ries and eating them was much easier than untangling my line.

But now, on this bridge, I understand what my father tried to teach me: patience and stillness. I look at him and smile.

"*Ciao*, Twiggles," he says, his trademark leave-taking. He is gone, and I am alone in the profound evening silence.

Later, I call Mom and tell her about crabbing. For a long moment, she is quiet. Does she think I've lost my mind? That I see ghosts? When she finally answers, she says that Dad always did have good advice about fishing.

She reminds me that *ciao* can be a greeting or a farewell.

So, thank you, Dad. And *ciao*.

Private Horrors
By Steve Gordy

Berlin, March 1944

The *Berliner Dom* was in flames from an Allied bombing. A garland of fire licked at the cathedral's great dome, embers and smoke rising in the almost windless air. As Erwin walked by, the massive structure looked like a heretic from a medieval woodcut, screaming in anguish at the encircling flames.

He'd barely escaped the flames himself. After the Meiringen incident, he took refuge in a hayloft a short distance out of town. A lightning bolt from a mountain thunderstorm had set the barn on fire. In the ensuing confusion, he'd put several kilometers between himself and the town. He'd reached Lucerne several days later, where he caught a train to Munich.

I got here just in time for the next act. The British had started intensive bombings of the capital in the fall. The Americans, still licking their wounds from the beating the Luftwaffe had given them in 1943, had been absent until a few days ago. March was scarcely underway when a force of almost 700 American "heavies" had struck the factories in the northern and western sectors of the city. A tremendous air battle resulted. Rumor had it that nearly half the German planes sent up to oppose the first big American strike had been destroyed or disabled.

No matter how many of the Yanks we knock down, they're bleeding our fighter squadrons to death. The burning church was well behind him now. Lost in thought, he'd wandered into a residential area. Just ahead, an apartment building had been leveled, tendrils of smoke still rising from the wreckage. Such sights were common nowadays. It seemed odd that the destroyed building had been hit in the raid; the hardest-hit areas were a long way off. *The American bomb-aimers are as lousy as the English. Must have been strays, or else they aimed at the wrong place.* As he drew abreast, two things caught his eye.

One was a small girl in a blood-spattered frock atop the pile of rubble. With infinite care, she picked up a loose brick, dusted it and tossed it aside. She repeated this act again and again, "Where are *Vati* and *Mutti*?" As he walked away, she began singing a nursery rhyme.

The other thing he noticed was an unexploded bomb amidst the ruins. There were words on the outer casing in some foreign language, possibly Italian. *Are the Italians bombing us, too?* The mad girl, the live bomb, the burned-out dwelling, all seemed as lifeless and remote as pictures in a gallery.

Berlin, February 1945

"You are a traitor!" Roland Freisler screamed as he waved a folder containing evidence at Erwin. The prosecutor, a red-clad scarecrow, leaned toward the defendant and bellowed, "The proof is here that you have given military secrets to the enemies of the Reich."

As Freisler paused for breath, the keening of an air-raid siren echoed in the courtroom. Guards hustled the prisoners down a staircase into the shelter and herded them against a wall away from everyone else, lest their criminality contaminate the court officials.

Erwin was resigned to death. His thoughts wandered to past encounters with the reaper. *French, Americans, Spartacists, Socialists, Jews, all of them wanted to kill me and they always failed.* The irony of being executed by his own people inspired in him no deep reflections. *God is dead. We left him in a trench at Verdun.* In the bunker, the rumble of bombs and the murmured prayers of some of his fellow defendants were the only sounds.

A new sound intruded, a treble whine rising above the bass notes of the background noise. The whine became a whistle, climbing in pitch, until a voice from the crowd shouted, "Get down!" The prisoners sprawled in a tangle of shackled arms and legs. A roar filled the chamber, followed by a pressure wave, a cloud of concrete fragments, a noxious fog, and the clunk of solid shapes falling.

Erwin had time only to think, *This is the end*, before an impact against his head hurled him into darkness.

"Freisler is dead." An emotionless voice cut through the fog.

Erwin drew in a deep breath and began coughing; the air was foul with dust, gases, and the warm smell of fresh blood. When he forced open his eyes, he saw the prosecutor a few meters away, his body crushed by a fallen beam. Unaware of his own voice, he said, "Thank God, thank God, thank God."

"On your feet." He looked up into the one-eyed stare of a submachine gun.

Berlin, March 1945

"On your feet!" A Gestapo man entered Erwin's cell and pulled him upright. "You're about to make a trip."

He said nothing. *If this is the end, at least I outlived Freisler. How will they do it? Firing squad? Guillotine? Hanging?* He walked out of the cell, emotionally detached from everything. At least when he was dead, he would no longer have to endure the stink from the clogged toilets, the teeth-rattling cold and wetness that clung to the walls, the inedible meals. As he shuffled down the prison corridor, he had the sensation of watching someone else, as though he were outside his body.

Two surprises awaited him. The first was pleasant; in the day room, his hand and foot shackles were removed. The second surprise quashed this fleeting hope. Two guards hustled him to a supply room. The private behind the counter handed him a neat stack of clothing and a common soldier's field kit.

"What is this for?"

"Shut up, Private Halsbruch. You're back in the Wehrmacht now and they don't put traitors on trial, they execute them."

"Where am I going?"

"To the Oder front. You can negotiate with your Red buddies over a rifle barrel."

The Lost
By Robin Lewis

Just outside of Tulsa
we stop for fuel and rest.
My lover drops into sleep
an easy peace.
It is a rare gift—
I wait for the same.
When we wake
my hand is on her soft stomach,
the other behind her head
entangled in her hair.
The bed sheets, sticky and sweaty,
wound round our legs
like spider webs.

Then it is another day.
The sun is wild and destructive—
the dashboard chaps and cracks
and beneath is yellowed foam—
canyons and crevices
we will never explore.
Next to me she dozes—
the open window
blows her hair into her face.
I think, she is lovely,
so perfectly lovely.

We will buy duct tape
to soothe the dashboard.
In time, we'll forget
the way it's newness
opened out before us
an undiscovered country.
And if we turn wrong
on purpose
and new horizons rise
before us out of mists—
out of the unimaginable depths of time—
if we turn west
and drive away into sunset,
forgetting ourselves,
who could blame us
for being lost?

Elvis Lite
By Bob Strother

I heard about it on the car radio—Matt Cordell, doing a "Tribute to Elvis" at the Gunter Theater—and thought it would be just perfect.

Vicki and I were new grandparents, and she'd been spending most of her days—and nights—helping take care of the baby. She needed a little time away, a little distraction, a little fun.

Since our marriage 15 years ago, I'd managed to help her overcome an unnatural obsession with the Bee Gees, and, like me, she was now a huge fan of the King. I'd seen Elvis live at the Omni in Atlanta about a year before he died. Vicki never had. This would be the next-best thing.

I called the theater box office. "Are there any good seats left for the Matt Cordell performance?"

"Let's see. Matt Cordell . . . Matt Cordell . . . ah, here it is."

My hand began to sweat on the telephone receiver. Would there be any tickets left? The Gunter Theater was awfully small.

"Yes, sir. As a matter of fact, you're the first person to call."

"Wonderful. I want the best seats in the house. What do you recommend?"

"Well . . . third row, center would put you just about eye level with the performer's . . . uh . . . belt.

"Great. I'll take two."

***

We arrived at 7:50 p.m. and took our place with 37 other enlightened theater-goers, nearly packing the first three rows of seats. Unbelievable. I was embarrassed for Matt before I'd even seen him. Would I see him? If it were me, I wouldn't come out.

"It's kind of an intimate crowd," Vicki said, scanning the rows of empty seats behind us. "Do you think he'll come out?"

I smiled at her and nodded confidently. "Sure."

She was staring intently at the stage curtain. "I hope he does a lot of the early stuff, you know? Like 'You're a Heartbreaker' and 'Young and Beautiful,' things like that."

We both thought Elvis's early music was his best.

"What I read about the show was that he'll be doing Elvis at about age thirty," I said, "so if we're lucky, it'll be all black leather and 'Blue Suede Shoes.'"

Then the lights went down, our hopes went up, and the announcer said: "Ladies and gentlemen, please welcome . . ."

And Matt cruised out, not in black leather, but looking more like a '56 Caddy Eldorado – powder blue jumpsuit, white-walled shoes and belt, and chrome studs out to there. His first song, "A Little Less Conversation" was from the 1968 movie *Live A Little, Love*

A Little. Not exactly what we'd hoped for.

I gave Vicki a weak smile and she squeezed my hand.

For the next two hours, we waited for the rowdy, rockin' echo-voiced guitar man of the Fifties. We yearned for "Lawdy Miss Clawdy" and got "For the

Good Times"—for "That's All Right, Mama" and got "The Wonder of You"—for "I Got A Woman" and got "In the Ghetto."

***

We did learn a few things that night. First, Elvis recorded 995 songs during his career.

"So," Matt said, "if you didn't hear the songs you wanted tonight, check us out in Pigeon Forge on Fridays and Sundays. We change the songs with every performance."

There was promise in that statement, but the last time I was in Pigeon Forge was 30 years ago. I have no plans to go again.

We also learned that there are 3,800 Elvis impersonators in the United States alone, and that in 2004, Matt won first place in a national "Tribute to the King" competition.

Finally, we learned that Matt Cordell was a nice kid. He told us he didn't claim to be an "impersonator"—said he didn't talk or act like Elvis unless he was performing.

"I was a fan first," he said. "Then I was lucky enough to become a tribute artist. Now, I just want to help keep the memory alive."

He brought his mom and dad with him on the road. Mom worked the stage, making sure he had water and scarves, and pretending to sing backup to the recorded music tracks. Dad was in the lighting booth.

***

The last number ended and Matt left the stage to as much of a roar as 39 pairs of clapping hands can make. Mom came down to the edge of the stage and handed out a couple of unused scarves.

"I know you were disappointed," Vicki said. "But I still loved it."

Maybe it was better if you hadn't seen the real thing. "Well, that's what it was all about. I'm glad you enjoyed it."

We were making our way down the row when she asked, "Don't we still have the *young* Elvis CD in the car?"

"Uh-huh, I think so."

"Let's open the sunroof and play some of his early stuff really loud on the way home."

I squeezed her shoulder and smiled. "Sounds good to me."

Behind us, just as we went through the doorway to the lobby, one of the men who'd been sitting in the front row started singing: *"Don't be cruel, ooh-ooh-ooh, to a heart that's true."*

I glanced back. He had one of the scarves around his neck. "That'd be thirty-eight hundred and one, I guess."

Vicki took my hand as we left the building and winked at me. "Give it a few minutes," she said. "I'm betting that before we make it home, there'll be thirty-eight hundred and two."

The Winter Before the Flood, He Crawled into Himself

By Sally Arango Renata

He slept through ice singing on branches,
the clamor of buds pressing through bark,
he slept as water bounded past rocks
and trees, to cover his nose and feet.

His woke to koi tickling his toes,
to weightless waves of morphine.
If you have a place, I have some fish
he said, *Some are fourteen inches.*

(For Bret Addison Smith, 1955-2009)

With childlike delight he swam
through the doors of sand castles,
mastered the movement of his once-
frozen legs. *I can walk now,* he said,

talking to me, or someone named Tom.
That's great, I say, wishing we had talked
like this before the flood, before the piano
began playing the last notes of his song.

Food as Religion
By Paddy M. Bell

<u>Part 1</u>

In the name of the Father and of the Son and of the Holy Ghost.
The one who eats the fastest gets the most.

Like that superstition about getting married when the minute hand is rising, meals in my house were served punctually at 7:30 a.m., 11:30 a.m., and 5:30 p.m. A sacred ritual.

Mom seemed to be always in the kitchen, preparing or planning not just savory nutritious meals, but color-coordinated ones with complimentary tones of brights and softs, primaries and secondaries, warms and cools. The color issue was very important to her. She dreaded the white-on-white menu that Dad would request: pale boiled spare ribs, egg noodles, mashed potatoes, and the omnipresent white bread. My father was prejudiced that way—only white bread allowed. Not one speck of grain, nut, or seed. And then:

"Mother, what's for dessert tonight?"

"Cinnamon tapioca, thumb-print cookies, rhubarb pie, and Yankee notions."

"Oh, not much time for baking today, huh?"

That's right. These would be considered meager dessert offerings. Meager or not, they were only for the virtuous who had cleaned their plates. Leaving anything on a plate was a sin, an insult to the cook, and disrespectful to starving children, especially those in faraway Asia. I wondered how a hungry child there could know about two brussel sprouts left uneaten in Ohio. I admit to finishing off those pygmy cabbages not so much out of respect for the Chinese children, as for the hope of a Yankee notion. Yankee notions? Those are amoeba-shaped scraps of piecrust dough, spread with butter and cinnamon-sugar, and then baked. Delicious.

Once the last notion crumb was savored, fasting was the commandment until the next appointed hour. That pre-McDonald's era offered no opportunity for sin by sneaking out for mid-meal snacks. The fast-food establishments were yet to arrive, but the locals in my little town could eat at The Goody Shop, J&J's, or Frisch's Big Boy. My family rarely entered these diners. Dad would comment:

"Imagine those Franklins going to the Big Boy every Friday!"

"Shameful to be seen out paying good money for food so often."

"Thank the Lord we don't have to go out to eat. Nothing beats Mother's cooking."

Really?! Then why did my stomach twist into knots at every family communion? Why? Because the anticipation of the delicious and colorful presentations was followed by dread—the fear that perhaps something would go wrong with a pork chop, a biscuit, or a pancake—the fear of a food fight!

Not the slapstick flinging of mashed potatoes or cream pies—I mean food *fight!* And my Dad could battle a fried egg for hours! With the eggs, it was usually due to accidental breaking of the yolk during the frying process. Didn't matter that in short order the yolks would be stabbed through with a piece of toast, and their glutinous innards oozing all over the plate. For Dad, every sunny-side-upper had to have an intact yolk. Mom never countered with much defense, just a knowing smile and hope that the next eggs would be better.

So at times a skirmish did erupt over a broken yolk, a tough pork chop, or a less-than-flaky biscuit. It was beyond me, however, that an under-seasoned chicken thigh could result in war. Dad thought any cook worth her salt (groan) should serve perfectly seasoned food. The only thing that upset him more than having to salt and pepper his food, was seeing anyone *else* reach for the Kitschy Campbell Soup Kid's salt and pepper shakers.

"You do realize that you're insulting the cook, don't you?"

If a guest left even a morsel of food on the plate, it might be:

"Something wrong? My wife's cooking not to your liking?"

These were prime-time cringing moments, especially if the guest happened to be a playmate or boyfriend. I just prayed there would be no scuffles, let alone an all-out war.

My parents had every right in the world to quarrel over typical concerns like money, jobs, in-laws, and children. But there was never a voice raised over these things—only food. I marveled that a biscuit could launch a holy war, or salt and pepper could shake the walls of Jericho. I wondered what could possibly be the offense of wheat bread, and worried if it was a mortal sin to eat when the minute hand was descending.

Sometimes food is religion, and sometimes food is sin.

I confess to breaking the "no-eating-between-meals" commandment with one quirky neighbor who became my occasional playmate—most often during Lent. She was a pasty child with Shirley Temple curls, crinolined dresses that accentuated her skinny knobby-kneed legs, and a prissy bedroom lined with Madame Alexander dolls in glass cases. Her idea of fun was arranging and rearranging those collectibles, and lining them up in alphabetical order according to the countries they represented.

"Hey! What do you think you're doing to Little Miss Holland?" she would ask. "Don't open that case!"

"She's suffocating in there, along with the rest of these Madames. They need fresh air and sunshine like my dolls."

"These dolls are not like your stupid ones that you drag everywhere you go. Your dolls are beat up and filthy!"

"Are not."

"Oh yeah? Well, what about Tiny Tears, huh? What happened to her?"

Somehow this question caused a lump to materialize in my throat and a burning sensation behind my eyeballs. So after committing the snack sin with her, I raced home to ask Mom what happened to my dolls.

"Oh, Honey, you plain wore them out. Poor Tiny Tears was so waterlogged from all you fed her that she rotted from the inside out. Yes, Baby, you simply loved your dolls to death."

I overfed Tiny Tears and killed her? How could that be? No dolls were loved as much as mine. I certainly never subjected them to the claustrophobic conditions of glass cases! So why *did* I play with that child curator of dolls who was my polar opposite?

Butter and sugar sandwiches on soft Wonder bread. Scrumptious works of the devil. But let there be no doubt, that's what makes sin a sin—it's so good that it must be bad. The way I saw it, those butter-sugar sandwiches were my reward for tolerating that freakish child. Playing with her was penance enough.

My sinful ways continued in my tween years when I took babysitting jobs based on the snacks in the cupboards. One family in particular comes to mind. They had a creepy old house with drapeless naked windows (perfect for Jack the Ripper to peer into), and two bratty and constantly snotty-nosed children. But a can of Charles Potato Chips and cold bottles of Coca-Cola made the snot bearable. Coke and chips were seldom found in my house, for the one and only between-meals indulgence for my family was Sunday-night popcorn.

Just before *The Ed Sullivan Show*, Mom would haul out a heavy pot, pour oil in the bottom, dump in the kernels, and shake that pot on the burner, the lid on tight, but with that little vent opened to let out the steam. The popped corn was dumped into the turkey-roasting pan, drizzled with melted butter, and salted. Then Dad sat in his chair, the roaster on his lap, and my brothers and I lined up with our pastel Tupperware bowls, saying, "More please?" Great ritual, that was. Watching *Ed* and happily munching away on that popcorn.

Every Sunday night that is, except during Lent when popcorn was sacrificed. Oh, how I craved it those 40 long days between Ash Wednesday and Easter Sunday. I asked if I couldn't give up something else—anything else—and keep the popcorn.

"No. Popcorn it is."

"Well, what if I do something *more* instead of giving something *up*? Like extra chores?"

"No, Honey, it's about sacrificing something special."

Today, I could enjoy buckets of popcorn, butter-sugar sandwiches, or chips washed down with Coke any old time I'd like, but it seems I have lost all such cravings. Perhaps this supports one of the beliefs in the religion of food: the sinfulness of something is magnified by the degree to which it is desired. Got it. But I don't yet get the doctrine of food as both virtue and vice. I'll have to sleep on that one.

> *Now I lay me down to sleep*
> *I pray the Lord my soul to keep.*
> *If I should die before I wake,*
> *I pray I've just had chocolate cake.*
> *Amen*

Part 2

Every Saturday afternoon, it was off to church for Confession, my brother and I making up sins on the way, trying to come up with something new. What *are* the sins of eight- and nine-year-old children besides forbidden butter-sugar sandwiches? Of course, at the time I didn't know I was a murderer of dolls through water torture, or I could have told that. Confession was always followed by the weekly pilgrimage to the real "holy sanctuary"—the meat locker.

"Put on the gloves, Honey. Don't want to get freezer burn on your little fingers," Dad said as he slipped the bulky duct-tape-like mittens onto my hands and pulled them up to my bony elbows, rendering me totally incapable of grasping anything with those silver paws.

Then to my brother, the same words every week: "Now Barty, get our key off the rack and let's go in."

I followed close on my brother's heels into the immense freezer, a catacomb of preserved, butchered flesh. The icy air burned my nostrils, and the smell of frozen carcasses made me gag. Right aisle, fourth vault.

"The key, son."

Reverently, Dad opened the locker . . . the chamber . . . this sacred vestibule. Counting, checking of dates, and rotating of packages were followed by the selection of a few slaughtered sacrifices.

"Hang the key back on the hook like I taught you, son. Turn the tag so our name is showing. That's right. Good boy. Now home we go."

Pseudo-hunters returning from a pseudo-kill.

I hated this gross mission, not understanding that it was not just about packages of meat, but that it was a statement—a statement to all that this clan had food and would survive. Besides the meat cache, my clan had a stockpile of canned fruits, vegetables, sauces, and juices, all in neat and colorful jars, labeled in my mother's perfect lettering. An abundance of everything that could be eaten. Plant, grow, harvest, can, eat, eat, EAT. Dad used to say of Mom's ornamental flowers, "Unless we can eat them, what's the point?" What *is* the point? What's the deal about food? Food the issue, always the issue.

My mother was seven years old in 1930. With her six siblings gathered around the kitchen table, I imagine a conversation like this:

"One for you, one for you, one for you, and . . . no, Francis, only one piece."

"He can have some of mine."

"No. He's got plenty to eat."

"Hey, that's *my* potato!"

"Pancakes again? I thought Fridays were meatless, but it's been every day!"

The Depression had a death grip on that family. Grandpa, a skilled woodworker and cabinetmaker, had resorted to digging ditches for the WPA, determined to keep his family fed during those dark times. When he trapped rabbits, my mother's repulsion was overshadowed by the excitement of meat on the table.

"Save the rabbit's front legs for your mother, children. That's her treat."

"Boys, we'll try fishing tomorrow. Maybe we'll have some luck in the Fox River."

The luck of the Irish had run out on my eight-year old father in 1930 after his daddy was injured while working for the railroad. The Depression hit them far worse than my mother's family.

"Cornmeal mush again? Will we never see meat?"

"Now Maw did a fine kidney stew last week."

"Have more bread and milk gravy, Son. Pepper it good."

"But it doesn't taste a bit like meat."

"You boys need to get down to the creek and catch some turtles and frogs if you ever hope to see anything resembling meat."

"But I'm hungry, Maw."

"Just go to bed and sleep—you'll forget about the hunger pains. You'll forget."

I sensed that it was something worse than the Depression that my parents couldn't forget. But what? Now in their mid-80s, Mom and Dad eat like birds, even wrapping up leftovers from a shared meal at Captain D's. Yet still they talk about getting a freezer and filling a pantry with food they'll never live long enough to eat. Why this obsession?

"What is it about food, Dad? Why is it so sacred?"

"Don't ask a question, Honey, unless you want the answer. Just don't ask."

* * * * * *

Inside a German prisoner-of-war camp in 1944, my Dad, a young B-17 pilot, was about to learn from fellow prisoners the powerful connection between cigarettes and living to see another day.

"Bartsky, the only way you'll survive is to join us here."

"Not doing it. I'm just going to sleep."

"Ain't gonna work, man. Ain't gonna work at all. Sleep brings no cure for this. Come on."

"I said NO, DAMMIT!"

"It helps, buddy."

"With what? Does it make the pain go away?"

"It just helps ease the hunger—here—a nice American Chesterfield. You'll see."

"My Maw always held that the body is a temple to be kept pure."

"Well there's no temples in this hellhole."

"Damn, I can't seem to stop my fingers from shaking to light the thing."

"Come on, flyboy with nerves of steel. Light 'er up!"

He did then, and does now. Today, his numb fingers still shake as he struggles to steady the match. Frostbite injuries from a three-day death march those many years ago in a brutal blizzard make even the simplest tasks difficult. It is painful to watch. But many things are painful to watch, and I have recently come to realize that the food obsession is indeed something more than the Depression and a small boy gigging frogs and trapping turtles for a bit of meat.

"Cigarettes here aren't just for smoking. They're currency, and they spend big."

"Got me a copy of *Mutiny On The Bounty* and a pair of socks for only a couple of filters."

"Well, food is all I wanta buy with the little fags. Just food."

At first, it was cigarettes well spent when Red Cross parcels were still getting through. Those early days revolved around the opportunity to eat, the clocks set and adjusted according to chow time. But into the second year, the buying power of cigarettes shrank to almost nothing. A combination of a bloat of the prison camp population from 20,000 to 100,000, and the cutting of supply lines meant no food—nothing to buy with the precious Chesterfields.

Days were spent scavenging, foraging for anything to eat. In the beginning, a trapped rat was skinned and cooked, but soon the skin and bones were eagerly devoured, and cooking became optional. When the rat supply vanished, cockroaches became the quarry, about the same time prisoners began sucking on rusty nails for the iron. A good day would be finding a rotten potato, a putrid cabbage leaf, or a morsel of the brown bread—the source of my father's prejudice.

The bread was a concoction of animal and insect parts, garbage, glass shards, and who knows what else, all baked into some unnamed brown filler substance. So when Dad saw bread of any color than white, or with any dark bits in it and he said, "Hey! Don't eat that bread. Those specks of shit in it might actually BE SHIT!" . . . it wasn't a joke.

After Liberation and the end of the war, Mom and Dad's secret marriage vows contained promises of never being hungry. My mother vowed to take care of him, and she kept that promise—kept it and stayed true to it like her faith . . . her religion . . . our religion: Food.

So I understand that Dad endured physical rigors, psychological tortures, agony and desperation beyond imagining, and spoke barely a word of these times and this war for almost 60 years. Yet I remain baffled that someone who once was grateful for a raw rat, a crunchy cockroach, or a rotten cabbage stalk could go to war over a tough pork chop or an under-salted chicken thigh.

But I suppose that near-starvation could convert someone into a religious zealot with food as the focus of faith, a focus worth fighting for. After all, wars have been started, empires overthrown, men and women slaughtered, and civilizations decimated, all in the name of religion. Why not in the name of food?

Give us this day our daily bread,
and as is the tradition,
Amazing Grace we humbly pray
in thanks for this nutrition.

Then armed we'll be to go to war
against the competition.
As long as first we Praise the Lord
then pass the ammunition.
(and the gravy, please)

AMEN

EPILOGUE

Approximately six months after writing this, Dad was admitted to the hospital for tests. "I'll be back home tomorrow," he said, picking at a dinner tray, swallowing a scoop of mashed potatoes and a single bite of Boston cream pie. "Can't hold a candle to Mother's."

Eleven days later, COPD/Pneumonia was identified as cause on his death certificate. Yes, I suppose. But for those 11 days, I watched him scoot food around, but not eat; watched him joke about the rubbery jello and lack of seasoning; watched him dance with Mom around the issue of not eating, like a parent trying to keep the magic of Santa Claus alive a bit longer for a child.

I watched him wage this final food battle, an act in total opposition to his life's purpose with my mother. Armed with a living will that restricted tube feedings and unnatural means of sustaining life, he courageously chose to shorten the ultimate course to the ultimate end. Ironically, he simply stopped eating.

My mother misses him terribly, most intensely at mealtime.

Pass Christian, Mississippi Mission Trip
By Martha T. Robinson

July 2007

"Through wisdom a house is built . . . By knowledge the rooms are filled. . . ."
Proverbs 24:3, 4.

Picture the Gulf coast of Mississippi two years after Hurricane Katrina.

Picture a coastal highway with miles of ocean, closed beaches, ruined piers to the south and nothing to the north except a flattened landscape, weed-covered parking lots, and signs proclaiming, "We WILL be back!"

Picture an unfinished beach house, with 18 10-by-10 square posts supporting the floor of a house to be built, 13.5 feet above the flood plain.

Keisha stood before us the first day we were in Mississippi, holding an umbrella in the steady rain. She wanted to greet us, the new team from Rock Hill, South Carolina, who would continue the work that had begun. She wanted to thank us for coming, for volunteering.

We asked her to tell us her story: How had she survived? Where did she live? An emergency-room nurse, Keisha was on duty when Katrina hit. Earlier, she had sent her two small sons to stay with relatives in Shreveport, Louisiana, not realizing how widespread or how far-reaching the destruction from the hurricane would be.

Many families whose homes were destroyed had fled the area, deciding to relocate somewhere else. Keisha and her family chose to stay. They had been shifted from place to place, one time

living in a camper on her uncle's property. Currently, they lived in a FEMA trailer.

Her application for a home was approved; her home would be built by teams from North Carolina Baptist Men Disaster Relief. NCBM Disaster Relief had pledged to build or rebuild 700 homes in and around Gulfport, Mississippi by December 2007. At the time we were there, 564 houses had been completed.

The blueprint for the house showed three bedrooms, two baths, a living room, and kitchen, with a deck on the front. Stairs to the front door and to a side entrance would be added later.

Our team consisted of 24 members of one church, an equal mix of men and women. Most of the men were skilled in construction. Several women also had some skills with a hammer and nail gun. Although I had been on several mission trips, this was my first experience as a member of a construction crew. The only equipment I brought was a pair of newly purchased work gloves.

The first day, those team members with tool belts, knowledge, and experience climbed ladders to the floor above to build the outside walls. For those of us who were unskilled, it was a day of organizing supplies.

I found out how slippery the uneven ground was as I helped to move plywood out of the rain, but I was not alone as I slid down. By the end of the day, nearly everyone had at least one long smear of red clay mud on his or her jeans.

I also discovered how necessary the work gloves were. At least one red ant from the first piece of plywood managed to crawl into my right glove. After that, I was alert for the tiny creatures.

I was also dismayed to discover that I could not climb the ladders to see the work being done above my head. When the call was made for all hands on deck to help lift the first wall into place, all I could do was stay below and cheer from the sidelines.

At lunchtime, there was not a dry spot anywhere, and not an inch of dry clothing on anyone. We ate sandwiches, sitting under the house, the only shelter around. Rain dripped from the bill of my gold Disaster Relief cap.

Shortly after noon, the rain stopped. By the time we returned to the National Guard Armory, in Gulfport that evening for showers and supper, our clothes had been steam-dried by the 90-plus-degree sun.

What could I possibly do to help the team? I knew the answer was to do whatever my crew chief told me to do. Pick up this . . . Move that . . . Find the . . . Bring me . . . Hold this . . . Rake that. . . . With each request, I did what I could, to the best of my ability.

I was amazed to see how much was completed each day. By the end of Day One, two outside walls were up. By the end of Day Two, all four outside walls were up, as well as most of the framing for the rooms. On Day Three, the trestles for the roof were lifted into place.

While the men worked mostly up top, the women tackled the problem of fixing the deck. From our first glimpse of the house on Day One, Elaine noticed that the posts for the front deck were out of line with the rest of the house.

"About four inches," she said from the back of the van.

After walking around the worksite and examining the posts from every angle, Beth dropped a plumb line. Elaine was right: the posts were exactly four inches out of line.

New holes had to be dug. Amanda and Stevie found shovels and posthole diggers and began to dig. During the night, the holes filled with water. The next morning, we found a tiny frog happy to be swimming in his own private pond.

The debate continued: how were we going to get the posts into the right place? Finally, the feat was accomplished by using ropes, and the combined physical strength of all the women, including me, as well as a couple of men to lift the posts out and then into the new holes.

Earlier during the week, Keisha had brought her two sons to see the house. All of the mothers on the team wanted to make certain that the deck was a safe place for Jordan and Jamie to play. The next project for the women was to build the deck and banisters.

By the last afternoon, that project was completed. Emily, Donya, Leslie, Stevie, Julie, Amanda, Beth, Pansy, and Elaine posed for a photo shoot on the deck with the completed front railing and side banisters ready to slide into place.

Elaine exclaimed, "Look what the Northside women have done!"

At the end of Day Five, Keisha returned with her sons, her mother, and an uncle. How excited she was to climb the ladder to explore the rooms of her new house!

Later, at home, as I unpacked from the trip, I wondered what I had accomplished. I found the gloves that had protected my hands from wood splinters and more insect bites. Knowing I would never use them again, I started to throw them in the trash.

Then I recalled tossing water bottles to Leslie and Beth as they worked on the deck.

I remembered a comment Donya made. "Martha, you are the one who is keeping this entire team hydrated."

I was surprised as I thought of all the extra trips she had made to the only local convenience store open for miles around to purchase more ice, more drinks, or just to take the women to use the clean restroom facilities instead of the smelly port-a-potty at the worksite.

And then I realized that each of us, whether skilled or unskilled, had used what abilities we had to help the team complete the project. I was both proud and humbled to be a member of a team who built a house.

Postscript: Keisha, Jordan, and Jamie celebrated Christmas 2007 in their new home.

He Belongs to Mexico
By Billie Bierer

She hooked up her horse, Ned, to the buckboard. Before stepping up, she straightened her blouse and skirt and shifted the holster housing her .44 to a handy position. It was six miles into town, down a dusty road that had never improved over the eight-or-so years she'd lived in the cabin by the spring. The spring was how she'd come to stay here. She'd bought the place after the failed stagecoach route had given it over to auction. Travelers continued to use the route because good water was scarce.

It was a lonely existence, but she preferred loneliness to the aggravation that seemed to come with any long-lasting relationship with a man. The last man had left after only six months. She thought of all these experiences that had webbed through her life and supposed they made her the woman she was. She wasn't getting any younger, and she longed for a child. She tapped a rein to Ned's rump and sped him up into a slow jog. Her long dark braid bounced down her back. She reached up, tightened down her sombrero, and cast her gaze over her shoulder toward the western hillside. Behind her the jagged peaks of the Sierra Madres towered, hazy with dust that swirled skyward. She was ever mindful of the possibility of strangers.

***

She tipped her broad-brimmed hat to folks on the boardwalks as she came into the small town of Dusty Bend, and pointed Ned toward the general store. The horse didn't need direction. He was used to waiting there. When she stepped down from the buckboard, she tied Ned and went inside, the little bell above the door tinkling.

"Well, Hello Sandia," Bill Watkins called from the back of the store. "It's good to see you." Portly, middle-aged Bill came from around a long wooden counter to greet her.

"The prickly pear around my place are a good rich purple," she said. "I'm supposed to let Martha know when they're ready. She wants them for jelly. We wait too long, those stray Mexican cattle will come through and clean out every last one." Bill laughed just as his wife stepped through the back door.

"I heard that," Martha grinned. "I'm ready anytime you are."

Bill frowned. "I don't want you good-lookin' women out there in the desert by yourselves picking cactus berries." Bill was a big man but didn't look a threat to anyone. "Those blue eyes of yours, Sandia, would attract any lonesome cowboy."

She knew Bill was being a gentleman. "It isn't like we've seen a stranger in months around here," Sandia said with a laugh.

"And I'm forty, Bill." Martha gave her husband a playful punch in the belly. "Not exactly a spring chicken."

"Sandia there is the chicken and there are plenty of roosters drifting through. I think I'll go along. It won't hurt to lock up the place for a day. By the way, Sandia, that book you ordered is in."

The look of mild frustration left Sandia's fine oval face and was replaced with one of rapture. "Wonderful!"

"You sure do read a lot."

"I love reading about other people's lives."

***

Sitting three across on Sandia's buckboard seat, they headed toward the foothills of the Sierra Madres.

"They're just beyond the big arroyo, by the boulders." Sandia pointed southeast.

Bill frowned. "Ain't that Mexico country?"

Sandia shrugged. "Never gave it much thought. No one comes here." She squinted into the sunlight.

"Maybe we should give it thought, Sandia," Martha said.

Sandia laughed. "The spot I'm thinking of is only another fifteen minutes."

"Yeah," Bill shrugged. "We're here, might as well enjoy this fine day."

***

They carried burlap sacks, tops spread wide to catch the pears that they hit with sticks so they wouldn't chance a barb. Ned was tied loosely to an ironwood tree that provided shade down in the arroyo. They each had about half a sack of pears when a herd of Mexican cattle moseyed up the arroyo, bellowing and looking for afternoon shade. It was Ned's whinny that made Sandia drop her sack and hurry back toward him. Ned was now pulling to get free from the aggression of a mother cow. Not seeing any safe way to get rid of the cow, Sandia shot two rounds into the air to scare her. The herd turned away.

It was then that the vaqueros appeared. Coming fast around the turn at full gallop, sombreros flying, the man in the lead dressed in a tight black leather vest, matching pants, silver shining, his clothes traditional and clearly expensive. He rode a handsome black horse. Bridles and decoration jingled and glinted in the midday light. This was all too much excitement for Sandia's old gelding. Now free, he pulled sharply left and hauled the buckboard and himself toward home at a gallop.

"Damn!" Sandia screamed. The Mexicans reined in, laughing. That is, all except for the handsome man who scowled down at her and poked her shoulder with the barrel of his rifle, bringing her attention to his dark, accusing glare.

He jerked his head toward the other two men. "Put this one on board behind me," he yelled. Silver flashed again as his horse danced around her. The stranger's intimidating stare knifed down into her. "You're trespassing," he said.

She didn't reply.

Ned was gone. There was no chance to head home at all.

"Get the other two," he ordered once Sandia was aboard.

"You're kidnapping us?" Sandia complained.

A skinny Mexican said, "Senor, this man is pudgy." He pointed at Bill. "He will lame my horse."

The head man growled, "If that happens, shoot the horse and walk."

***

They arrived at a low-slung hacienda surrounded by ironwood trees and catclaw and creosote bush. The formidable leader let her slide off the big horse without assistance. He moved behind her all the way to the hacienda as if still herding his cows. Once inside, he pushed her into a dark room and slammed the door. She heard the lock turn from outside. There was a small table that held an oil lamp, which she lit with a wooden match that lay there. The room had no window and only a narrow bed against a wall.

When the man came back, she said nothing, but took the water he offered.

"Still don't feel like talking, Senorita?"

Her light eyes knifed into his.

"Suit yourself," he said and was gone.

After an uneasy night, he came again. "You're welcome to freshen up. I will show you the way and one of my men will wait in the hall outside the door in case you decide to try to leave us."

When he returned, he smirked. "I have been courteous and shown you great hospitality. Now it would pleasure me if you would administer liniment to my back and shoulders. I have been breaking wild horses and I am not as young as I once was. Also, I prefer a female's touch. My cook saves her hands to make bread." Amusement lit his eyes and she again glared at him. "You are a beautiful woman. It is too bad we cannot be friends. Come with me."

The man led her off to a room with a long hardwood bench. A shelf was pushed against one wall and lined with tiny bottles. She said nothing to him. And he reciprocated by not conversing, but handed her a bottle of oil to use. She had no choice.

He took off his shirt, taking great pains to fold it over the back of a straight chair. She willed her mind blank as she sometimes did when riding up into the hills where she would peer out over the empty vastness. This she had practiced and this she brought to herself now. She massaged the stranger's back and shoulders until her fingers ached.

***

Later, when she had rested, the man came to her again and ordered her back to the same room with the table. Expecting the same routine, Sandia retrieved a bottle of sweet oil and watched as he stripped off his shirt and lay down on the bench and turned onto his stomach.

His voice muffled, he said, "I could have killed you for trying to shoot my cattle."

Her mind not yet settled into its void, anger flared and she threw the sweet oil across the room where it hit the wall and splattered. She spat, "I shot to scare a cow that was trying to gore my horse. That cow was mean. If I'd been shooting to kill her, she would be dead and you'd have reason to kill me."

"Even in anger you have a pretty voice," he whispered.

She pushed back loose hair that had fallen onto her forehead and she bent to her task again, fuming over the man's audacity. What was it to her, if this man had a penchant for back rubs and no intelligence to determine who was a cow killer and who wasn't?

She sighed and rubbed his back. Without realizing, her breath caught as she watched the well-formed muscle roll beneath her kneading fingers. Her touch prodded between bone and muscle. Smooth russet skin gave way to her plying fingertips. A soft groan of pleasure escaped him.

He was muscled from hard use. She wondered about his life and about the things that he knew, wondered about all that he'd seen. His dark hair smelled of lemon water and curled along the nape of his neck, and his skin smelled of fresh-cut grass.

While she was thinking all these things, her hair, now loose from exertion, fell around her face. She was startled when he rolled over and stared up at her. Brown eyes knifed into blue as he reached up and pushed back her loose, damp tendrils. His hand gently cupped the back of her head and he pulled her face to his and kissed her thoroughly, expertly—a thoughtful, lingering kiss. She did not resist, and this, too, shocked her. Her heart hammered in her chest. This was no inexperienced cowboy. This . . . she had never experienced. In one swift motion, he swung from the table, scooped her up, and carried her to his bed in an adjoining room where he slowly undressed her without taking his eyes from hers. In her heart, she realized that this was a man intent on what he wanted and confident that he would get it.

"I will forgive the mess you made with the oil," he said and smiled.

Naked, he was as beautiful as the chiseled sculpture she had once seen in a book.

His lovemaking left her sated and spent. When he rose and turned his back to pull on his breeches, she whispered, "You aren't going to shoot me?"

"No."

"Do you always get everything you want?" She didn't see his smile.

"Why have you not asked my name? All women want to know their lover's name."

"You are not my lover. I am a woman you took."

Turning, he drew back. "Please," his eyes tightened on her, "you were a cooperative participant who has the unfortunate habit of running men off." He looked around. "This is my hacienda. I'm not leaving and you can't run me off from what is mine."

She inhaled sharply and sat up, pulling the cotton sheet around her. "You've been spying on me?"

He smiled.

Finally, she said, "A name is to be remembered only if the individual happens to be someone of importance that you care about."

He looked away, but not for long. His dangerous glare stilled her.

He said, "You read many books, yet you don't know yourself. I could help you."

She scoffed, "This is how you help?" Her sarcasm contradicted her feelings, because for the first time in her life, she was filled with doubt. Still, she knew he was toying with her. She asked, "What of my friends? Are they alive?" Her heart thudded with dread when she saw him run his tongue around inside his cheek. His jaw clenched and unclenched.

He inhaled and walked toward the open double window, his back to her again. He looked out toward the Sierra Madres. "I own fifty thousand acres. I own this hacienda. Three hundred men work for me. I run five thousand cows on my land and you don't care what my name is." He turned back toward her. "You are the woman who lives at Bonito Springs, Sandia Johnson."

"Yes."

With force, he continued, "The spring belonged to my family once long ago." He poked out his chest and straightened his shoulders. "I could claim that land. It was part of my country."

138

She frowned. "Before that it belonged to the Apache, and before that to God. It'll one day belong to God again, because I'm certain humans are only temporary on this Earth—but let's talk politics and spiritual beliefs after you tell me what you've done to my friends."

"Don't be insolent," he said, but not in an unkind way.

Sandia moved to the edge of the bed and drew on her shirt. "I'm merely worried about my friends. If you're any kind of a good man, you will tell me how they are. We weren't hurting your damned cows, we were picking prickly pear for jelly, for Christ's sake." She pulled up her split riding skirt and tucked in her shirt. He watched her every move.

"You are lovely. You have wonderful hands: capable, soothing." He reached out and traced his thumb across her cheek. "You have the face of an angel, and yet, you are stubborn beyond belief." He turned from her and looked out the window again. "Your friends are fine."

"When can we leave?"

"I'm considering what to do with you."

She scoffed. "You are considering what to do with me? You don't want to keep me. Being insolent is only a fraction of the trouble you would get by keeping me."

He spun toward her and rocked back on his still bare feet. "I would have something to look forward to, then."

"Like you, I do what I want to do."

He nodded. His voice as soft as a feather's touch, he said, "Yes . . . I can see you would be trouble. But, just so you know, you can return to me at any time. If only you were different, perhaps we could have married." He bowed in kingly fashion, only lacking velvet cape and crown.

***

He gave each of them a horse with his apology. She looked at him from aboard her new horse and asked, "What is your name?"

He laughed. "Now that you're going home with a gift, I am important enough?"

"You've surprised me," she admitted and lowered her eyes. And because, no matter how much she denied it, she felt something between them.

"I am Elias Salvador," he said, and again bowed in that royal fashion. "I hope your horse and buggy made it home."

***

Sandia also carried the gift of life back to her beloved Bonita Springs. When their son was born, she named him Elias Salvador Johnson. Elias was a beautiful baby and he grew strong and looked so much like his father that at times, in certain light, the uncanny resemblance gave Sandia chills. She had never lied to her son. He knew his father was only hours south.

Now, at 15, Elias wanted to know his father, but Sandia could tell him no more because she knew very little of the man who had bedded her at 30. The event itself was a secret pleasure she had held close all these years.

Then, as if called, Elias Salvador himself rode up in front of her cabin, leading another saddle horse. Her heart thudding, she screamed at her son to stay in the house, but her boy had looked out the window and gone, anyway. Her son was no longer a boy to be held by a mother's command. How could she blame him?

A graying Elias Salvadore nodded. "Sandia, it is good to see you. You have aged well." He sat back in his hand-tooled saddle, leather creaking, and looked over the rest stop. "This place has been cared for with a loving hand. My ancestors would be pleased."

She stood, hands on hips, glaring at him. "You're not here to talk about the bluebells I planted."

"No. I am sorry."

She believed him.

His face now looked pained, his sensuous mouth down-turned, his dark eyes somehow drooping. "I've come for my only son. He is of age and needs his father to show him the land that will one day be his."

She swallowed. Elias his only son! How could this be? This was a man of stature, a man of wealth who could have any woman and should have many sons. Her body shook with realization, her hands sliding from her hips.

He looked toward the Sierra Madres, but his gaze came quickly back to her and the boy. "He looks like me. I would have you, too, but . . ." He shrugged.

She gave a faint smile. "I'm willful."

He said, "I've honored your wishes. But, I have a son and I will have him now."

An unnecessary command, because his son also wanted him. She would give her son the same freedom she had been granted. He belonged to Mexico.

Sandia reached up and tousled her son's dark hair. "Take care of yourself and him. I love you both." She watched him run to the horse his father had led in behind his own.

"You are welcome at the hacienda, Sandia. I think it is not good to live alone." As they left, her gaze followed the faint mirage that was her son and the only man who'd ever cared for her.

The Good Husband
By Marilyn N. Smith

The path lay straight.
Bed of sand,
prepared with care.
Stakes, accurate
at every corner.
String lines, meticulous.
Bricks carefully chosen
and placed at convenient points
along the way.
Work slow and steady.
Once begun, no pause for rest
or the day's heat.
The completed walk exact.
No subtle shiftings.
No unevenness.
Nothing unexpected
to stub or trip.
The product of a fastidious man.
Later, at the direction of his wife,
he would arrange a stack
of smooth river stones to one side.
Later, he would hang her
wreath upon the door.
Later still, a bird would nest there.
Finishing touches to his solid work.
Each preparation, a caring.
Each precision, a kindness.
And every step leading
always
directly home.

No Time to Write
By Melinda Cotton

Bill asked, "Why don't you bring anything to read anymore?"

Recently, I discovered a very strong desire to write. I joined a local writer's group, but found myself showing up at our bimonthly meetings empty-handed 85 percent of the time. On the rare occasions I have read, the group seemed to like my writing. To answer Bill's question, I replied, "I don't have time to write."

A full-time litigation paralegal for the United States Attorney's Office, I find the work to be both physically and emotionally draining. I'm also on the board of the Palmetto Paralegal Association and Second Vice President of the National Federation of Paralegals Association, a wife, mother, daughter, sister . . . well, you get the picture.

I'm the oldest (though I prefer "first born") of four siblings, and the daughter of two parents with typical aging complaints and illnesses. I often act as my parents' "alarm clock" and call to wake them for doctor's appointments. I've always felt it was my duty to raise my younger siblings and take care of them. I'm always the "go to" person whenever a problem or question arises. I also have a 93-year-old grandmother who gave me quite a run for my money this past summer while my parents were at the beach.

Don't get me wrong; I love my family, and they are generally supportive of my burning desire to write—as long as it doesn't interfere or conflict with any of their schedules. With such a large close family, there are always birthdays, anniversaries, holidays, school plays, sporting events, etc. that everyone is expected to gather for. My husband's family is also close and lives nearby, creating even more opportunities for family get-togethers. The holidays are shared, meaning we eat two Thanksgiving dinners and two Christmas dinners. I don't believe I have the right to tell them I'm not joining family time because "I want to write."

I know the process of writing is a lonely one; you just can't sit amongst a group of friends or family and isolate yourself enough to write. Many times I've carried notebooks on vacations or weekend getaways, only to bring them back empty.

An exception is the family vacation I took last summer with my husband and son. We rented a two-bedroom oceanfront condominium on a barrier island in mid-Florida for two weeks last July. My husband towed our fishing boat, and he and my son went fishing nearly every day. I happily carried my beach umbrella, chair, sunscreen, reading book, and writing pad to the beach every day. On that private beach, I would write, read, walk, and write some more. I reveled in my freedom and wrote more in that two-week time span than in the rest of the year put together. I returned from vacation refreshed and excited, and couldn't wait until the next writer's group meeting to read my material. That feeling lasted for about three meetings, then nothing. I've not written a word since.

I used to think I had to have the right writing space to sit and create. So, I talked my husband into converting a spare bedroom in our house into a writing office for me. I painted walls and hung pictures. I even borrowed a roll-top desk and bought a glass-front bookcase for all my books. My library of books on writing and crafting a novel sit at the back of my desk, ready to be consulted while I'm churning out my masterpiece.

The first time I entered my writing room, I announced to the family, "I'm going into my room to write. Do not interrupt me."

Within a short period of time, my husband came to the door and poked his head in "just to see what I was doing."

Soon thereafter, my son hollered down the hall that I had a phone call. I hollered back, "Take a message, I'm writing."

Not long after that, my son came to the door to tell me so-and-so was on the phone and did I want to talk to them?

"No," I shouted. "I'm trying to write."

Within 10 minutes, my husband was at the door wanting to know what was for supper. I gave up.

A few Saturdays ago, I thought the sun, moon, and stars were finally aligning themselves in my writing galaxy. My husband was going to be working and my son was scheduled to take the SAT. I spent Friday afternoon and evening washing clothes and straightening up the house so there would be no excuse not to write the next morning. Then, while preparing dinner that night, the phone rang. It was my mom, which wasn't in itself unusual because we normally talk three or four times a week. That night, however, she wanted to know what I doing the next day.

Warning bells sounded as I hesitated. My heart rate sped up. It wasn't fair—it was supposed to be *my* Saturday, my *writing* Saturday. Hedging, I asked why she needed to know.

"Let's go to Orangeburg," she said.

"Orangeburg," I exclaimed. "What the heck's in Orangeburg?"

"Wicker," she replied. "I stopped in a store a couple of years ago and I want to go back and have another look-see. Might find a goodie. Wanna go?"

"But, Mom," I said. "Do you really think you should go? You just had that cortisone injection in your back last week, and we're supposed to be going to Charleston next weekend, remember? I don't want you to exert yourself in Orangeburg and then not be able to go to Charleston and enjoy walking around. Why don't you wait a few weeks and I'll go with you then."

I stirred the butter beans and held my breath. Please, please, I thought. I really wanted to write. It had been so long and I was afraid my writer's group was going to lock me out of the meetings for lack of participation.

"I really want to go," Mom said. "I've been cooped up in this house for three weeks and I'm going stir crazy."

I opened the kitchen cabinet and grabbed three dinner plates, set them on the counter, then reached for the silverware.

"But, Mom," I said again. "What about Charleston?"

"We'll just consider Orangeburg a test," she said. "Besides, I'll have a whole week to recover before we leave for Charleston."

"I think it's supposed to rain tomorrow," I offered, taking the salt and pepper shakers down from the shelf and placing them beside the dinner plates.

"Not according to what Ben said on the seven o'clock report." Mom always refers to the weather reporters as if they are her personal friends. "Besides, I really want to go and I'm going, with or without you. Of course, if you don't go, I'll have to drive myself and that will probably add to my back and leg pain. But you think about it tonight and call me in the morning. We can leave bright and early."

We said goodbye and hung up. I called the boys to dinner. After saying the blessing, I looked at my husband and said, "Guess what, honey, I'm going to Orangeburg tomorrow."

He raised his eyebrows and lifted a spoonful of mashed potatoes.

"For what?" he asked.

I looked at him and said one word —"Mom."

"Never mind," he said, biting into his meatloaf and shaking his head. After being a part of my family for over 30 years, he knew he didn't want the details.

The next morning, I drove my mother to Orangeburg and we enjoyed a wonderful day together. As I've said before, my family is supportive of my writing. If I'd told my Mom of my writing plans for Saturday, she would have never said an-

other word about Orangeburg. But then we wouldn't have spent the drive to and from Orangeburg talking, and we wouldn't have spent hours walking through the wicker warehouse, and she wouldn't have found the beautiful wooden sculpture that looks like a huge coral reef that she uses as a room divider in her new room at the beach, and I wouldn't have enjoyed a cup of the best damn clam chowder I've ever put in my mouth. We had a blast.

Nonetheless, I regress. When I told Bill I didn't have time to write, he replied, "Why don't you write an article about why you don't have time to write?" So here we are.

I can no longer use the excuse that I don't have a place to write—I just need an armed guard posted at my door to keep the family out. In talking with other writers, I've learned that many of them hold full-time jobs and have families, yet they somehow find the time. Could it be that my desire to write isn't as strong as I believe it is? Or is it simply that I'm busy enjoying life and spending time with my family and friends?

At a recent writer's conference, I had the privilege of sharing the dinner table with a published mystery writer. When she asked what I wrote, I told her how much I wanted to write, but never seemed to have the time. I mentioned a few of the issues discussed herein and she very wisely said, "Well, honey, it just might not be your season to write." She went on to explain that just as everything happens for a reason, all times have their seasons. So maybe it's just not my season.

So, I'll continue spending time with my loved ones and writing when I can. I'll continue taking notes and enjoying life experiences that one day, maybe, can be written into my book.

How to Succeed in Sales
By Maureen Sherbondy

Ask about the product—
the wiggler, whomp, or widget
no matter how dull or useless
it seems. Request a guided tour
of the plastic factory,
point and nod, take in the vrum
of machines, act like a child
in front of the monkey cage
at the zoo when noise vibrates,
and vrooms and whirs swirl
around you. It doesn't matter,
just smile, stare, feign interest,
open your ears, listen, say little.
Ooh and aah at the apparatus,
the metal claws, the buttons, levers,
red and green diodes. Let him talk
no one else does, not his wife
or kids or shop steward, not
the 40 overworked employees.
He'll renew the account, refer
you to friends. Just shake his hand,
smile on the way out, your fingers
caressing the money tree rising
inside your lined pockets.

Walls
By Michael Hugh Lythgoe

Near the wall . . . I saw visions of God.
　　　　　　　　　—Yehuda Amichai

Cracks in The Wailing Wall are full of prayers.
The President tucks his secret petition
In the temple wall between ancient stones;
A journalist steals the private prayer.
Every separation is a link. Listen to silence.
Will God tap in code? In solitary confinement
A prisoner wonders if he will always be alone.
Up against the wall! A French firing squad
Slays Madrid's defenders in Goya's *The Third of May*.
A wall may be a dark memorial, art others say.
Walls are not all for mending, or neighborly.
Only two North American cities had walls:
Quebec's still stand; Charleston's are history.
Lone prisoner in his cell listens, hears
Scratches on the wall, crawls closer.

The Clown
By Richard Lutman

It was time for the clown to do something about the young bareback rider. She'd teased him long enough with her swirling mixture of dirty sweet innocence, and dared him with a sexual magnetism that she was just beginning to understand. Tonight the two of them would celebrate her 18th birthday with a picnic, something she would not easily forget. He'd see to that.

He came out of the warm night smells of dew and coffee toward the main circus tent. The large half-mastiff next to the cook trailer watched him, straining at the heavy chain that was attached to its neck. He stopped and crept slowly in the direction of the dog.

The dog's large head tilted as he followed the clown with fierce glittering eyes. He jumped up, waved his arms and hat, and the dog sprang at him in a frenzy of barking. The hot, blue breath curled against the lights of the trailer.

He laughed. The smell of crushed grass filled the half dark and a cricket started up, chirping loudly.

He stood in the shadows outside her trailer where he could see and hear her through the low window.

She sat in front of a mirror, dressed in a long black dress and a yellow silk blouse. She carefully studied herself, then put her finger into her mouth and slowly pulled it out so her lipstick glistened. Her pale husband lay on the sofa behind her, his narrow shoulders between two pillows.

"Are you going out again?" he said. "It's your birthday."

"What if I am?" she said. "It's none of your business where I go."

"It is! You're my wife and I want you here. I've planned a party. This is the most important birthday you'll ever have, you're a woman now."

"I don't care what you've planned. I don't want to be with you. You disgust me. You always have. And you smell of medicine. The hell with your party! I've got better things to do."

"I love you," he said. "Doesn't that mean anything to you? I've been in love with you ever since that night you first came to me in southern Ohio. Do you remember how frightened you were of lightning?"

"No. I don't."

"You shook so much I was afraid that something was going to happen to you. Then afterward, you fell asleep in my arms. Your looked so innocent you nearly broke my heart."

"I don't remember," she said. "You have it wrong."

"Do I?" He sat up. "The accident wasn't my fault."

"But you fell," she said. "You said you wanted me to be the first to see your new handstand on the trapeze."

"I thought I could do it."

"Then you were a fool."

"If I was it was because of you!"

He rose painfully and put his hands on her shoulders, then kissed the top of her head. The girl turned to face him.

"Your hands are ice cold. I wish you wouldn't touch me when they're like that. It's like you're dead."

She poured out a glass of whiskey and drank it quickly. "I have to go."

She started for the door. He reached out to grab her. She pushed him away as hard as she could. He staggered back and caught himself against the table. Then she stepped out into the night with a picnic basket hanging from her arm.

"Bitch!" he said as he lurched to the door. "You bitch! Someday you'll come back and I won't be here! Then what will you do? Who else would want you? You forget who made you what you are. Without me, you'd be nothing. Nothing. Do you hear? How long will it be before he sees you for what you really are? How long?"

She had already disappeared into the dark where the clown waited for her.

Her long dress rustled over the grass and he smelled her perfume, which reminded him of dry roses. He thought of how arrogant and beautiful she looked, just like one of the horses, waiting to finally be broken and tamed.

They walked side by side to the nearby wood and stopped when they came to a clearing. The clown took the basket from her and placed it on the ground, then sat against a tree where he could watch her.

"I never thought I'd get out of there," she said. "I don't know why I ever married him."

"I don't want to hear about it."

"Think you're really something, don't you?"

"I'm nothing more than a circus clown. You know that as well as I do."

"Fuck you!"

He lighted a cigarette and watched her through the twisting smoke as she slowly lifted her skirt up and took off her shoes, then let the skirt fall. She caught his eye.

"But let's not talk about such things anymore," she said. "What did you get me for my birthday? I hope it's a necklace. You know how much I want one."

The clown crushed his cigarette out.

"Can't you at least give me a hint? I don't like it when you tease me."

She held up her hand to the domed quietness of the sky as if trying to catch the essence of the night. The shadows were warped and black. The clearing smelled of pine and diesel exhaust. Near the moon, the shadow of an owl hooted. She tensed.

"When an owl hoots it means bad luck," she said.

"If you believe stories like that."

"Don't you?"

"No."

"What do you believe in?" she said.

The echoes of a stream came to them from behind the dark shapes of the rustling trees. She looked at him.

"The night when nothing is as it seems," he said, "and death, which brings eternal night."

"I don't want to hear about death," she said. "I want to live forever, then I can do what I want and no one will be able to stop me."

She spread out a tablecloth and placed cheese, bread, fruit, and wine on it, then poured out two glasses and sat cross-legged on the ground next to him.

The crystal pattern of a spider web caught her eye. She watched the black shadow crawl outward and shivered.

"You can't escape the circus," he said. "There's no place else for you to go."

"No," she said. "I want more. So much more."

"Then you'll have to pay the price. Won't you?"

The clearing stretched before them, overgrown with tangled roots. The clown lifted his glass to his lips once again. His silver throat gurgled. She smiled at him, then stood and began to pace.

"I remember the first circus I went to," she said. "Every young farmer from miles around went down with his girl, or wanting one. As you got closer, you could see the circus loom up larger and larger until you were swallowed up. How I loved it. I knew then that I wanted to be in the circus, to live that kind of life. I had to wait more than an hour for the Ferris wheel. Then up I went in a creaking yellow seat where I could see where the sun went down. The churches of the next town, and all the people, they looked so small and far away. It was like what God must see. . . .

"And I fell in love with a clown that night. I couldn't have been more than six or seven. He had a large ugly smile and a huge round nose, as red as it could be. His hair stuck out from the sides of his head like cotton candy. I didn't know his name—I just clapped my hands and called out 'Hey clown. Hey clown.' When he caught my eye, he bowed and smiled."

The circus sounded far away. The hoop of the Ferris wheel stopped against the sky and winked out. One by one, the lights of the midway darkened until there was nothing left of the circus but the sound of the fluttering flags at the top of the tents.

He rose to his feet, stepped forward, and reached for her breasts. For a moment, she left his hands alone before she pushed him away, as she usually did. This time he tightened his grip.

"You're hurting me!"

She squirmed and twisted, tossing her long hair across him. He laughed and gripped her harder.

With a free hand, she slapped him. When she looked at it, her fingers were covered with streaks of glowing silver that seemed to mingle with the pulsing of her blood. He laughed again and shoved his body against her. Her knees buckled and she slid to the ground. He held her tightly by the throat, almost suffocating her, and with his other hand tore at her blouse. His body shuddered against her. She kicked, clawed, bit his hand, and broke loose, rising to her knees. He pushed her down hard into the grass and she felt the strength go out of her and fought not to faint.

Slowly her cries grew less until they subsided into uneven gasps. She smelled cool grass and semen.

"A bitter joke," she said, looking down at her breasts, which were now bright silver in the moonlight. "Now I'll go back and tell my husband what happened. I know exactly what he will say; 'Poor little girl, how I pity you.' Then I'll cry and ask if he can forgive me. He'll look at me and say, 'You shouldn't ask forgiveness of me. I have nothing to forgive.' Then he'll be very tender and say that he is to blame. Would you do that?"

In the distance, lights shone cozily from windows. Inside those windows, children were kissing their fathers goodnight. And wives stopped to smile at their husbands, discussing the events of the day and the plans for tomorrow.

The clown lay back on his elbows. His laughter echoed off the silent trees and out into the night. In the dark behind them, the excited horses stamped and snorted in their cages.

The Nature of Things
By Marilyn N. Smith

The snake was not waiting.

It was beside the path.
It was still.
It was lovely.

It lay in an
early summer
patch of sun
cushioned
on layers
of old oak leaves
in skin newly
exposed and shining.

It did rise up,
taunting
with bold snake eyes,
tempting
with ancient witching tongue.

It did pause before
turning
to point the way,
and leading,
silent
among barely
stirring, hoary
garden depths.

It did not curve back
to see or hear or know
if I were following.

The snake was not waiting.

The World's-Gone-Crazy Cotillion
By Bob Strother

Rita Feldspar was on her forth draft Budweiser, and her speech hovered in that fleeting space between philosophical and slurred. She tapped the *Union Daily Times,* folded on the table in front of her, and sought to bring her companion into focus. "Can you believe it, Debbie? I wasn't even invited—and I'm her *mother!*

Deborah Reese, on her third beer, and obviously no stranger to the role of "Sympathetic Listener," smiled ruefully. "It's clearly an injustice."

Rita let her eyes stray back to the *Times* article on the Union Cotillion, being held later that evening: *Amber Lynn Feldspar is the daughter of Dr. and Mrs. Harold Feldspar of Jonesville, and Rita Sommers Feldspar of Gaffney. She is sponsored by her grandmother, Mrs. C. Richard Feldspar, and will be presented by her father. A student at Converse College, Miss Feldspar will be escorted by Daniel Conner Underwood.*

A tear rolled down Rita's cheek and landed in her beer. Then her lips thinned and she felt color rise in her cheeks. "I'm going, damn it, invited or not. I *will* see Amber presented to society."

Debbie nodded. "That's the ticket, girl. Show 'em you're not just somebody's trash to be left at the curb." She signaled the waiter for two more beers.

.....

An hour earlier, Mrs. Mason Evans Farnham III—Eleanor to her friends—stood before the hastily erected stage at one end of the Lakeview County Club Grand Ballroom. White taffeta bunting cleverly concealed the platform's rough wood underpinning and provided a nice contrast to the black velvet backdrop. In front of the backdrop, along the rear of the stage, workers from Union County Rent-All arranged white pedestal columns, topping them with baskets of lush greenery.

"It's lovely," said Winnie, Eleanor's assistant, who had silently appeared at her side. A worrier, Winnie's fragile hands were never still. At the moment, she wound a white lace handkerchief around her forefinger.

"Yes," Eleanor said, "it is lovely. It's a pity there aren't more girls coming out."

As cotillion director for the past 15 years, Eleanor had seen the numbers of debutantes dwindle sharply with each arriving spring. And with each annual affair, she felt the sands of Union society slipping through her fingers—saw the cultural base of tradition, manners, and deportment crumbling at her very feet. "Have you seen any of the girls yet?"

Winnie nodded and continued working the handkerchief. "They're beginning to arrive now."

"See to them, won't you?" Eleanor said. "I have to check with the caterers."

.....

Leigh Anne Windom sat stone-faced in the backseat of her father's Lexus, grinding her teeth, arms crossed defensively across her chest. The drive to the country club had been less than pleasant, to say the least. She caught her father's eye in the rearview mirror.

"This is humiliating, you know. What if my friends read about this in the newspaper?"

"Friends?" James Habersham Windom said. "Don't you mean fellow radicals?"

Leigh Anne bit her lip. A sophomore at Furman University, she was a card-carrying member of NOW, Equality Now, and the Young Democrats—hardly the associations her father had in mind when he'd forked over the highest private university tuition in the state.

"Now, James," her mother said, "Leigh Anne is only expressing herself, finding her own identity." She gave her daughter a quick over-the-shoulder smile. "I wouldn't worry, dear. I'm sure your friends never read the society pages, anyway."

The Lexus pulled to a stop outside the rear entrance of the country club. Leigh Anne emerged, grabbed her accessory bag, and slung the $2,000 ball gown roughly over her shoulder. "Just know I'm doing this under protest," she said, slamming the car door and trudging grimly up the steps to the entrance.

.....

Kimberly Jane Harper stood in the dressing room, laying out an array of cosmetics and studying her reflection in the mirror, when Amber Feldspar poked her head through the doorway.

"This where we're supposed to get dressed?" Amber asked.

"Uh-huh," Kimberly said, gesturing to the long countertop, inlaid with Italian marble. "There's some space over here for your stuff."

Though the two girls had gone to Union High together, they were not close friends. Amber had always been too free-spirited for Kimberly's tastes, dating a large number of boys and—if the rumors were to be believed—sleeping with most.

"I don't know why we had to be here so early," Amber said. "It won't take me more than twenty minutes to get dressed and ready."

"But it's our night. Don't you want to look perfect?"

"Nobody's perfect," Amber said, tossing a small zippered bag onto the counter. Then she walked to a large closet at the rear of the dressing room and hung her gown next to Kimberly's. "I'm gonna wander around, kill a little time."

"Suit yourself," Kimberly said, smoothing a layer of foundation on her forehead and cheeks.

.....

Tiffany Cook Carter slipped in through the rear entrance of the club and stood just inside the door, ball gown draped over one arm, a queasy feeling in her stomach. She leaned back against the wall and waited for the nausea to pass. Tiffany was worried—way too worried. For three months, she'd been praying for her period to start, to no avail. That by itself would be enough for anyone to bear. Now she worried that her gown—the one she'd been fitted for weeks ago and picked up only this afternoon—would be too small to accommodate her thickening waist.

Down the hall to her right, she saw Leigh Anne Windom talking to Winnie Lepley and three other women. Thinking she could inquire about the dressing area, Tiffany made her way toward the small throng.

"Leigh Anne," she heard Winnie say, "I'd like to introduce Mrs. Frank Odell Simmons, Mrs. James Hershel Wakefield the Second, and Mrs. H. Clay Evans Johnson—all former debutantes presented here at the Union Cotillion."

Leigh Anne extended her hand to one of the women. "Pleased to meet you," Leigh Anne said. "May I call you Frank?" Then to another of the women, "Do you prefer James or Hershel?"

"Well!" Winnie interjected as the women's mouths gaped. "Look who's here. It's Tiffany Carter. Hello, Tiffany. My, you're positively radiant this evening. Are you using a new blush?"

Tiffany felt her stomach roil and she placed one hand on the wall for support. "I . . . I'm looking for the dressing room," she stammered.

Leigh Anne glanced at her and raised an eyebrow. "Come with me." She took Tiffany by the arm.

.....

Amber Feldspar pushed through the side door of the country club and felt a cool spring breeze ruffle her hair and caress her skin. Then she caught a whiff of marijuana and turned to see one of the caterers—a young Hispanic man—leaning against the painted brick wall, cupping a fat doobie in one hand. A look of surprise, then alarm appeared on the young man's face. He raised a finger to his lips.

"*Buenas tardes, senorita.* Don't tell—OK?"

Amber cocked her head and gave him an appraising look. He was *mucho* good-looking, with smoldering Antonio Banderas eyes, and dressed in tuxedo trousers and a white serving jacket that stopped at his narrow waist. "Not a problem, *hombre*. Mind if I have a little hit?"

He replied with a gleaming smile that Amber thought might darken the late afternoon sun, and offered her the joint. "But of course," he said.

.....

Leigh Anne stood by protectively, holding both of their gowns, as Tiffany gulped noisily from the water fountain, then straightened and took a long breath. Best friends in high school, they'd stayed in touch regularly during their freshman year in college. Then Tiffany had met Roger, and the friendship had taken a backseat. It had been months since they'd talked.

"Are you ill?" Leigh Anne asked.

"No, damn it, I think I'm pregnant."

Leigh Anne gave a low whistle. "Roger?"

"Yes, of course, Roger. I'm not like Amber Feldspar, you know."

"Does he know?"

A tear glistened on Tiffany's cheek. "No, I . . . it's only been two months."

"You *have* to tell him," Leigh Anne said. "Either that or get an abortion."

"*You* might be able to do that," Tiffany said. "I don't think I could."

"Then tell him. He's your escort, right? Tell Roger tonight." Leigh Anne helped her friend to her feet and they started for the dressing room. "He's got all the proper credentials—his family's from old money. Y'all can get married. Your parents will be thrilled."

.....

Eleanor Farnham opened the big double doors to the club kitchen. Women in aprons and white-jacketed servers bustled about the gleaming stainless-steel countertops, squeezing pastry bags and stacking trays of hors d'oeuvres. Eleanor searched the area fruitlessly for Mr. Douglas, the head caterer. Finally, she spoke to a small brown man chopping cilantro on a wooden cutting board.

"Where can I find Mr. Douglas?" she asked.

The man looked up briefly, then shrugged. "*No se, senora.* In the back, maybe."

Eleanor strode toward the door marked "Storage and Receiving," wondering if she would eventually find it necessary to learn the Spanish language. The storage area was crowded with racks of round tables, stacks of chairs, and tall rows of shelving full of linens and serving accessories.

"Mr. Douglas?" she called out. "Are you here?"

When there was no answer, she moved forward, picking her way along the rows of shelving. As she neared the end of the third row, she heard the murmur of voices and soft laughter. Eleanor turned into the row and stopped dead in her tracks.

"Oh, my goodness!" she said.

Amber Feldspar and a young Hispanic man turned sharply in her direction, then struggled to untangle themselves. Amber straightened her blouse and smoothed the front of her skirt. "Oh, hi, Mrs. Farnham," she said. "Diego was just showing me some, uh . . . things."

As the waiter hurriedly busied himself with table linens, Amber walked—*a bit unsteadily*, Eleanor thought—to the end of the row.

"Are you all right, dear?" Eleanor asked.

The girl's eyes looked a little glassy, but perhaps it was just a trick of the low lights in the storage area. "Oh, sure," Amber said. She took a deep breath and gave Eleanor a big smile. "I'm just great."

"Well, we'd best get you back to the dressing room. We'll be starting before you know it." Eleanor took the debutante's arm, lest she inadvertently trip and fall, and began guiding her back toward the kitchen. "By the way," Eleanor asked, "is that a new perfume you're wearing?"

"Yeah," Amber said. "Some kind of herbal thing, I think."

.....

Leigh Anne Windom peeked out the door of the dressing room and saw her friend Tiffany sitting in the hallway alcove next to the rear entranceway, crying piteously. Her boyfriend, Roger, slumped beside her, looking as if he'd been sucked completely dry of all his bodily fluids. *Poor kids,* Leigh Anne mused, *and I thought I was miserable.* She heard footsteps and voices then, and turned to see Mrs. Farnham, Amber Feldspar, and the girls' escorts making their way down the hall.

Leigh Anne waved to Miles Willis, her own escort. Miles was nice, if somewhat dull, and thoroughly intimidated by Leigh Anne's assertive nature. With him were Craig Houston, Kimberly Harper's escort, and Danny Underwood, a recent conquest and current escort of Amber Feldspar. The group stopped in front of the dressing room doorway, the guys' eyes darting around to see if they could catch any of the girls in a state of undress.

"Over here, boys," Mrs. Farnham said, pointing to the alcove where Tiffany and Roger were now whispering furiously. As the boys gathered, Tiffany sprang up from her seat and rushed into the girls' dressing room.

"Are you OK?" Leigh Anne asked.

Tiffany dabbed at her eyes and pulled open the gown closet. "I told him," she said. "He didn't take it well at all."

"He'll come around," Leigh Anne said. "It just takes a while to get used to the idea."

"I hope so," Tiffany said. "I just . . ." She clutched at her stomach, her shoulders jerked, and then she braced herself with both hands on the closet doorjamb. "I . . . I . . . oh, Jesus, Leigh Anne, I'm going to—"

As Leigh Anne watched, her friend yakked up the remains of a particularly colorful lunch all over the front of Kimberly Jane Harper's brand-new coming-out gown. Tiffany swayed on her feet and her face lost all its color.

"Oh, my God!" shouted Kimberly. "She's puked on my gown!" She ran to the dressing-room door. "Mrs. Farnham—Mrs. Farnham, oh God, Tiffany puked on my gown!"

Tiffany's boyfriend was first through the door, followed closely by Danny Underwood and Mrs. Farnham. Roger caught Tiffany under the arms and turned her toward a nearby chair just as she erupted for a second time. Danny couldn't stop in time, lost his footing in a puddle of slick glop, and went down in a tangled heap.

"Ahhh! Son of a bitch!" he cried, grasping at his ankle and writhing on the floor.

Almost as if by magic, Winnie Lepley slipped through the doorway and appeared at Mrs. Farnham's side.

"Winnie," Mrs. Farnham said. "Call nine-one-one for Mr. Underwood. Ask them to come to the rear entrance and to use no lights or sirens. Leigh Anne, please get a wet towel for Tiffany's forehead."

"But what will I do about my dress?" Kimberly asked.

Mrs. Farnham looked at Kimberly over her eyeglasses. "You, Kimberly, sit and be quiet." She turned to Amber. "And you, Amber, find yourself a new escort—fast, understand?"

"Yes, ma'am," Amber said.

Leigh Anne went to get a towel for Tiffany. Despite all of her protestations to the contrary, she thought, *this is way better than the Equality Now meetings.*

.....

Trailing in the wake of a large family contingent, a tipsy Rita Feldspar managed to slip into the country-club foyer despite her lack of invitation and proper dress. She found the restroom and hid in one of the stalls until she heard the orchestra warming up for the prelude to presentations. Then she eased out and entered the ballroom, where rows of chairs had been arranged. Moving carefully to maintain her balance, she found a seat in the first row.

"My daughter is being presented tonight," Rita said to the blue-haired biddy in the adjacent seat. "Amber Feldspar."

The older woman drew herself in like a turtle and edged as far away as possible. Rita wondered if she should have munched a couple of Tic-Tacs before arriving. Then the lights dimmed, the orchestra sounded a brief flourish, and the emcee's mellow voice filled the room.

"Good evening, ladies and gentlemen, and welcome to the eighty-eighth annual Union Cotillion . . ."

.....

Eleanor Farnham watched nervously from stage left as the debutantes and their fathers assembled stage right. Winnie stood at her side, ready to cue the appropriate escort's entrance after each girl was announced and presented.

Eleanor took a deep breath as the emcee said, "Miss Tiffany Cook Carter . . ."

Tiffany and her father stepped onto the stage while the emcee extolled the young girl's heritage and accomplishments, ending with her recent election as incoming president of the Junior Class at Winthrop University. Following Tiffany's presentation, Winnie gave Roger a gentle push, and the young man strode zombie-like across the stage and offered his arm.

As the couple approached her, exiting the platform, Eleanor could not help but notice the mascara-laden tear tracks glistening on the girl's cheeks. Her heart leapt. *Oh my,* she thought, *what a moving experience it must be—this coming of age and acceptance into society.* She was about to embrace the girl when Tiffany suddenly bolted from her escort and ran sobbing toward the rear hallway. For a moment, Eleanor thought to follow her, but then the emcee's voice began once more.

"Miss Kimberly Jane Harper . . ."

Kimberly and her father marched across the stage, heads held high as the emcee continued. Eleanor noted, with no small measure of satisfaction, that the newly fashioned sash completely covered the gown's badly stained bodice. And no one would ever guess the sash was made from a strip of leftover taffeta stage bunting. Resourcefulness, she'd reminded the girls, is a key factor in becoming a successful woman in today's world.

"Miss Leigh Anne Windom . . ."

Eleanor was just beginning to relax, just beginning to feel the rush of relief that always crept over her as the presentations were nearing their end, when the unthinkable happened. Leigh Anne rose sweetly from her post-presentation curtsy—then thumped a fist hard against her chest and extended her closed hand high above her head.

"Oh, my," Winnie gasped. "That's the Black Power sign, isn't it?"

Eleanor struggled to maintain her composure as Leigh Anne, her nervous-looking escort, and a fuming, florid-faced James Windom swept past her. She felt a timid touch at her elbow, and Winnie whispered, "Only one more to go."

.....

It took a moment for Rita Feldspar to notice the tuxedoed man leaning down next to her. When she finally looked, the man said, "Ma'am, I've been asked to escort you to the exit."

"But my daughter's being—"

"I'm sorry, ma'am, but according to Doctor Feldspar, you're here without an invitation." The man took her hand, pulled her gently from her seat, and began walking her toward the rear exit.

The emcee's voice boomed: "And now, our last debutante, Miss Amber Lynn Feldspar . . ."

Rita stopped and turned as Amber and her father stepped onto the stage. "Oh, there she is. My, isn't she lovely?" The grip on her arm tightened, and Rita felt herself being dragged up the narrow aisle. At the exit door, she looked up at her captor. "Couldn't I watch from the doorway—for just a moment more?"

The man sighed and nodded. "For just a moment."

"Oh," Rita whispered, "look at her escort. How handsome he is . . . and those eyes . . . just like Antonio Banderas."

.....

Eleanor fanned her face with a folded cotillion program as she tried to recover from watching one of the hired help march out to escort Amber Feldspar off the stage. He'd come out of nowhere, it seemed, in his serving jacket and tuxedo trousers, perfect teeth resplendent in a *café latte* face. Amber had practically glided off the stage on his arm.

"Winnie," Eleanor finally said, "is it just me, or has the whole damn world gone crazy?"

Winnie smiled sympathetically and said nothing, her fingers working feverishly at the frayed white-lace hanky.

Kudzu
By Will Jones

Summer's green Tarzan tapestry,
Winter's gray mourning shroud,
Southern roadside drapery.

Brave Front
By Betty Wilson Beamguard

It's your need that moves me,
not the desperate clinging sort
that causes one to flee,
but the hidden kind that only shows
in your eyes in unguarded moments,
the loneliness you conceal so bravely.

The kind of need that makes
the mother in me long to hold you,
the friend in me want to keep you laughing
the sister in me hope you'll confide your pain.

It's your need that draws me,
that and your little-boy grin.

Blood Kin
By Elsie Holcombe

nobody looked like her.
five aunts, four uncles,
nineteen cousins,
even Mom and Dad.
they all said she was
"chosen" and loved.
but at night when
she knelt to pray,
tears stained her day's
false face and she begged
for blood here on earth,
or beyond.

Herbert Slago's Revenge
By Gene Hines

Herbert Slago was a bit actor who played Uncle Eugene in two episodes of the popular television series *The Three Sisters*. But after two episodes, the actors playing the three sisters cut off Herbert's career in network TV at the knees.

"I can't stand him. Please, Miles, you're the producer, you've got to get rid of him." That was Sister Number One.

"I can't either, my God he's such a slob, I don't think he bathes every day." That was Sister Number Two.

"He stinks," said Sister Number Three. "My God, he's a pig, I almost expect him to oink or something. You've got to get that awful thing out of this show."

They killed Uncle Eugene with a heart attack. Herbert found out he was dead when he went to the studio to tape episode three.

"Oh, didn't anyone tell you?"

The opening scene of episode three began with the Three Sisters mourning the sudden lose of "Dear Uncle."

Herbert Slago was a fat, good-natured man who played fat, good-natured men, usually sitting on park benches feeding pigeons, in the backgrounds of movies and TV shows. He did commercials, too. His best spot was one for Budweiser where he played, as always, a fat, good-natured man—this time, on a couch drinking beer. They ran the commercial four times during the Super Bowl.

The Three Sisters was his big chance, the culmination of his dreams. He was the best middle-aged, good-natured slob in Hollywood and New York combined, and after all those years of park benches and commercials, he was getting the recognition he deserved.

Now it was gone.

"Thank you, Miles," said Sister Number One.

"Yes, Miles," said Sister Number Two.

"You did what you had to do; I couldn't stand that man around me, the pig," said Sister Number Three.

TV viewers knew each of the Three Sisters well. One was a standup comic with an HBO special under her belt. One was a slightly older woman starring in her third TV series. The third was a bad imitation of Madonna whose main talent was wearing very little clothing. *The Three Sisters* had an inane sexual innuendo every 45 seconds and an obnoxious laugh track; it promised to be a great success.

But now, Herbert Slago was out.

The injustice of it curled like a huge worm around Herbert's innards. He dreamed of doing unspeakable things to the Three Sisters. But, what could he actually do? Angry, really angry, for the first time in his good-natured slovenly life and there was nothing he could do about it.

He thought of some things, obscene phone calls, that sort of thing; he even picked up the phone once, but he put such ideas aside as unworthy of a man who once had a commercial broadcast during the Super Bowl. Nevertheless, the worm curled around his guts and grew.

Then Herbert did a thing he never even imagined he could do, an act of violence. He made the mistake of watching the last episode of the season of *The Three*

Sisters. He was OK, just feeling a little sorry for himself, until the fake Madonna said, "Gee, I wish Uncle Eugene was here."

Herbert went out into the garage, got a baseball bat, and smashed his TV screen into a thousand shards. He killed the fake Madonna and was standing there, panting like a rabid dog, with the murder weapon in his hand. The explosion when the bat went through the TV screen was like the bursting of a skull. "Oh, God," he said.

Then he thought of Wendell Chin-Yee. It just came to him. They say things don't just come to people, except in bad stories, but it did. Standing there, holding the Louisville Slugger and panting, surrounded by the shrapnel of his TV set, Herbert remembered Wendell Chin-Yee.

"My God," he said again. "Why didn't I think of that before?" He cocked his head back and laughed as he shouted, "a stroke of genius!" He did a jig of victory, the glass of the shattered TV screen crinkling under his feet.

He called his agent.

"Mack, I want Wendell Chin-Yee."

"What? Is this Herbert—?"

"I want Wendell Chin-Yee."

"Who the hell is—?"

"That guy, that Jamaican-Chinese guy who was with me on that *Tales from the Crypt* bit. Remember?"

"Good God, that was fifteen years ago."

"Come on, Mack, find him for me. You know the business, you've got the contacts, he's out there somewhere. Find him, please."

"You want me to find a Jamaican-Chinese bit player you haven't seen in fifteen years, is that right?"

"Yes. It's important, really important."

"Anything else?"

"Yes, another network show."

"Sure." Mack hung up.

Herbert hugged himself and did another little dance. He forgot that when they worked together in an episode of *Tales from the Crypt*—fat, bug-eyed zombies stumbling out of a foggy jungle—he didn't believe a word Wendell Chin-Yee said.

"You expect me to believe that?"

"I'm just telling you this hokey zombie crap is bogus, it ain't nothing like what we could do in Jamaica."

Herbert and Wendell were on the set, wearing their zombie gear and waiting for the techs to get the fog machine working.

Wendell said, "I can do this. I can do worse. I used to be an Obeah Man."

"A what?"

"An Obeah Man. Comes from Africa and it's a big thing in Jamaica. Better than Voodoo. I used to do it. Spells. Make people do anything. My people, the Chinese, been in Jamaica since the Eighteen-hundreds. They learned how to do it, too. Love spells, make bad things go away, make bad things happen, that kind of stuff."

"And you can do that?"

"Used to. Turned a mean old man into a tree stump once and all the dogs in town pissed on him, he was their favorite spot."

"I don't believe a word of it. You're as funny as this damn show."

But Herbert didn't remember that part about not believing what Wendell said. He was an Obeah Man. That's all Herbert wanted to believe.

But nothing happened.

Mack didn't call back. Maybe Wendell was out of the business. Maybe he was dead. Maybe he was a tree stump in Jamaica. Herbert called Mack again but Mack didn't return that call, either.

Herbert slipped back into his daydreams of the tortures he wanted to inflict on the Three Sisters. He saw a copy of *People Magazine* that said that each of them was up for that year's Emmy for best comedy actress. The rumor was that it just might be the first time an Emmy would be given to a group of actors, instead of just one.

Herbert cried himself to sleep.

Then Mack called.

"He's in the phone book," Mack said. "I looked in my old files. He lived in Covina in those days, so I figured there was a long shot that he still did. Different address and number, though."

Mack gave Herbert the number. Herbert and Wendell met at Starbucks.

"Well, look at you," Wendell said. "You're just as fat as you were then. But I knew that already," he said. "I've seen a couple of your commercials. Keeping busy, huh?"

"Yeah, pretty much."

They were sitting at a little round table sipping house brew. It had been a long time since *Tales from the Crypt*, so they sipped and looked at each other out of the corners of their eyes.

"Did you see any of my *Three Sisters* stuff?" Herbert said.

"I heard about it, but I don't watch much TV anymore, not since I quit the business. Hell, my last bit was as a corpse on *X-Files*. Got out after that."

"What have you been doing?"

"A little here, a little there. Getting by. You know how it is."

It was the second cup of coffee before Herbert got to business. He said, "You still one of those obi men?"

"It's *Obeah* man."

"Oh, sorry. You still doing it?"

"A little here, a little there."

The palms of Herbert's hands were moist and he rubbed them on his pants. He forced himself to breathe slowly and easily. "Can you get back at people?"

"So what do you want, Herbert? Let's cut to the chase."

Herbert started breathing hard again. What exactly did he want? Something awful, of course, but what? The plague? Cancer? Snakes in their beds? Run over by a truck? Cancel the show? "I don't know, you're the obi man. Something bad, really bad."

"That doesn't help much," Wendell said. "Could you be a little more specific?"

Herbert saw each of the Three Sisters in his mind. They were beautiful. "Make their teeth rot, turn black, and fall out," he said.

Wendell looked at him with disgust. "That's it? That's not even worth my time."

"OK, you think of something."

"It's your call."

"Could they be eaten by sharks?"

"Sure, why not?"

"Could you turn them into tree stumps, like you did that old man?"

"Whatever you want. The possibilities are limitless."

Herbert never thought it would be this hard. It's one thing to want to get back at somebody, it's another thing to pull the trigger.

"Make them a hundred years old?"

"Sure."

"Make them zombies?"

"Whatever."

"Really?"

"Look, Herbert, if it's that hard for you, maybe you should forget it. You're just too nice a guy."

"No, dammit. They ruined my career. I'll never get another network show. They deserve the worst you can do." Herbert's face was red.

"OK, Herbert, I think I've got it," Wendell said.

"You do?" Herbert smiled.

"Here's the deal. We do a kind of generic thing. It's kind of a *what they deserve* spell. How about that?"

"I don't understand."

"We just tell old Xango to give them what they got coming, let him figure it out."

"Who's Xango?"

"Never mind. The less you know, the better. He'll like it. Most of the time people tell him what they want. I'll bet he's sick of giving people cancer. He gets to use his imagination, he'll like that. I'll go home, get my oanga bag and get right to work on it."

"Can you do it before the Emmy awards?"

"Sure."

The Three Sisters would get exactly what they deserved, whatever it was.

Herbert was happy. He felt a great weight lifted away. He felt light and gossamer as a feather cradled in the breeze. "Thanks," he said.

Nothing happened.

Herbert called Wendell six times. The conversation was always the same.

Herbert, in a whining voice, "Please. *Now*. I can't stand any more waiting. Please—"

"It takes time, Herbert."

"What have you done?"

"I've done it all. A little chanting. A little dance or two. Lots of incense and cajoling. A little pixie dust for good measure."

"When, then?" A sob in Herbert's voice.

"Patience, my friend, patience. They'll get what they deserve. Trust me."

So Herbert waited. "I can't stand it," he said to himself over and over again. He couldn't sleep and he couldn't eat.

Then it was time for the Emmys. Herbert didn't have a TV anymore and he couldn't watch, even if he wanted to.

Besides, it wasn't going to happen. Nothing was going to happen at all. . . .

"Miles, tell us what's going to happen," said Sister Number One.

"Yes, Miles, please," said Sister Number Two.

"Will they give it to all of us?" said Sister Number Three.

"At least one of us is bound to get it." said Sister Number Two, again.

"I think you'll all get it," Miles said.

"Oh, bless you, Miles," all the Sisters said.

Herbert went to bed early the night of the Emmy Awards. He took sleeping pills and tried to forget that Wendell had let him down.

He was going to miss it all.

The Three Sisters were gorgeous. Works of voluptuous art. Their black dresses cleaved to every dip, whirl, and curve of their bodies. They glided, legs and hips and glistening lips, to the limousine waiting to take them to the Emmys.

Even Miles was stirred by their beauty. "You ladies look just wonderful."

Herbert slept.

They drove through the city, the sights, sounds, and smells of the street shut out by the tinted windows and the purr of the limousine.

"Music, ladies?" Miles pushed a button and an undertone of Whitney Houston surrounded them. "And, a bit of champagne." Another button and a bottle and four glasses arose from a consol. "It will calm you."

They were floating through the city in a perfect world.

"I don't feel so good," Sister Number Three said. "I'm getting a headache."

"Just nerves, drink some more champagne," Miles said.

They drove on, toward the glittering lights.

"I feel awful," said Sister Number Three.

"Here, I've got some Tylenol. Fix you right up," Miles said.

The lights of the city drew the limousine on like magnetic beams.

"Come to think of it, I'm not feeling so great, either," said Sister Number One.

"Oh, for goodness sakes." Miles handed the Tylenol bottle to her.

By the time they got to Wilshire Boulevard, all of the Three Sisters had headaches. They were gulping Tylenol like candy.

Then, Sister Number Two squeaked. She opened her mouth to say that she felt awful, too, but all that came out was the squeak.

"What was that?" asked Sister Number One. "It sounded like a baby."

"That wasn't a baby, that was you," said Sister Number Three, pointing her finger at Sister Number Two.

"I couldn't help it," said Sister Number Two.

"She just tried to talk and hiccupped at the same time." Miles took a drink of champagne.

Then Sister Number Three squealed, a short high-pitched sound.

Sister Number Two laughed. At least she meant to laugh, but she squealed, too.

They all laughed, but it came out a chorus of squeals and squeaks.

Miles pushed a button and light bathed the inside of the limo. He looked at the women. They seemed all right, except for one thing, their beautiful faces shone back at him in pink as bright as a Mary Kay Cadillac.

"Holy shit," Miles said.

"What's wrong?" all the Sisters in unison.

"Must be the light." Miles turned it off. "It was nothing." He took another swallow of champagne.

They rode on, anticipating the night.

Herbert slept.

"Something stinks in here," Sister Number One said.

The Three Sisters looked around at each other, sniffing the air.

"Don't you smell it, Miles?" said Sister Number Three.

"No, I don't . . . wait a minute . . . what *is* that?" Miles said. "My God, it's awful!"

"Phew, open the windows," said Sister Number One.

Miles pushed the buttons and the windows swished down, the heat and sounds of the street flowed in like a river.

"It's getting worse," said Sister Number Two.

"What can it be?" said Sister Number One.

Sister Number Three leaned over and sniffed Sister Number One. "My God, it's us," she said.

They all sniffed one another. "We stink," they all said together, and their voices ended in squeals.

Then a grunt.

Another squeal.

A snort.

"Miles, what is this?" the voice was unrecognizable, a snort and a grunt between each word.

Miles squeezed himself into the corner, away from the sounds and smells.

"What's happening?"—squeal and grunt.

Miles turned the inside light on again. He jammed himself into his corner as hard as he could and threw up his hands in front of his face, a puny barrier against what he saw. "Stop!"

"What?" the driver yelled back from beyond the glass barrier. "We're almost there—"

"Stop!" Miles screamed, as if the word was the only one left in his vocabulary.

The limo stopped at the curb. There was a crowd on the sidewalk, waiting to see the stars walk into the Emmy Awards Show.

"Who's that?" went up and down the sidewalk.

The driver jumped out and opened the passenger door. Miles's screams exploded out of the car.

The crowd stepped back.

Cameras snapped and whirred.

The crowd laughed and applauded, smiles lighting up the night.

Herbert missed it all. He slept until noon the next day. It was 1 p.m. by the time he found out that the Three Sisters had turned into pigs, little pink piglets in black dresses with red-painted snouts.

For a few years, the Three Sisters made the rounds of the late-night talk shows. Three piglets in dresses and diamond necklaces. They told pig jokes and laughed and squealed with Conan O'Brian and David Letterman. But as they grew fatter, and turned into hogs, they weren't invited on the shows anymore. They considered an offer from *Ripley's Believe It Or Not*, down in Florida, but turned it down. Rumor is they are living in seclusion somewhere in Montana.

But Herbert Slago is still around. If you watch TV you can see him in the background, sitting on a park bench feeding pigeons or reading a newspaper. And, if you have one of those huge new TVs that hang on the wall, you'll probably be able to see the half-smile on his face.

October
By Marilyn N. Smith

The bridge disappeared
this morning.
As I approached the crest
it wavered and was gone.
The river, its traffic,
pale marsh grass, the shore
with its band of pine and oak,
all gone.

Trusting in what had
only yesterday been here,
I travel, borne on frail,
sometimes deceitful
memory, into the muted, soft
distortion of what is
today's downward span
and beyond.

Check Your Battleship
By Robin O'Bryant

My husband and I have always lived hundreds of miles away from our extended families in Alabama. We are used to loading up everything we own and taking road trips with our kids. My husband usually drives, reluctantly I might add, while I spend most of my time turned around in the passenger seat tending to the kids, passing out snacks, and picking up whatever toys they have dropped.

Usually somewhere along our route to Alabama, I will glance at Aubrey, our oldest daughter, and notice that she is asleep with the DVD player still running. To avoid turning around in my seat for the hundredth time, I'll whisper to my husband, "Zeb, is Emma asleep?"

"How am I supposed to know?" he'll say. "I'm driving."

"Zeb, look in the rearview mirror, OR pretend you are checking your blind spot and GLANCE at her to see if she is asleep."

"That's really not safe."

Is he serious? Does he realize that I drive with them in the car every day, and can keep one hand on the wheel, my eyes on the road, and still reach their baby dolls in the back seat when they drop them?

"LOOK AT HER!" I'll hiss at him.

"Yeah, she's asleep."

I'll turn off the DVD player and slam it shut.

In November 2007, we made the move from Savannah, Georgia to Mt. Pleasant, South Carolina. He was driving his car and pulling his motorcycle on a trailer. Because my car has the DVD player, I had our (then) 18-month-old and our 3-year-old in the car with me. We got into Charleston around dark, and as we were crossing the Ravenel Bridge, my cell phone rang. It was Zeb.

"Did you see that battleship?" He began to describe the USS Yorktown in vivid detail.

"What battleship?"

"The one we're driving over."

"I'm SORRY! You mean the one that's five hundred feet BELOW us, and a quarter of a mile BEHIND us? Are you for real? You're pulling a trailer, talking on your cell phone, and driving across a six-lane bridge you've never driven on before, IN THE DARK, and you can't look in the backseat to see if your child is sleeping?" I hung up the phone.

The next time we were in the car headed to Alabama and things got quiet, I asked, "Is Emma sleeping?"

"I don't know," he said. "I'm driving."

"Then just pretend she's a battleship."

Flood Tide
By David F. Westeren

To Magellan Crowne, all real truths were simple. Take Uncle Byron's favorite line, "red sky in the morning; sailor take warning." If you lived in coastal New England, you could bet your life on it. Fishermen like Mr. Sousa did every day. Maybe it was the salt air and long hours spent gazing beyond shoreline breakers to the misty origins of all waves. Maybe it just came along with youth. Yet at 17, and three weeks from her high school graduation, Magellan knew what she wanted. She simply just didn't know how to get there.

Over and over, she repeated the words silently like a mantra, until the words rose with the incoming tide of her emotion, surging, making her gasp before they crashed into the silence of the room: "We all want to believe we're on a journey. That's the foundation of religion, the basis of hope." Startled by the boldness of her voice, Magellan raised her head from her journal and closed her eyes. Her fingers fidgeted with the pencil, tapping out a heartbeat, trying to imagine back 300 years.

A night breeze nudged the curtains at the east window and whispered through fresh new leaves on the great locust tree outside on the corner of King Phillip's Highway. She thought about the ancient tree and about its crowning thorns that reminded her of Jesus's passion and the steadfast fervor of the Pilgrims. Hadn't Professor Landsford, from Brown University, told her mother the tree was the oldest surviving specimen in all of New England? This fact thrilled her with family pride and, at the same time, made her shiver as from a brush with mortality. Her pencil drummed faster, impatient for the inspired word, twirling at the tips of her hands. She breathed in the bewitching fragrance of the night.

Magellan opened her eyes to semi-darkness and returned to her story. She wrote in the present tense as Mr. Samuals had instructed. Magellan liked the way he had put it. The technique would imbue immediacy to her piece. She liked everything about Mr. Samuals because, simply, he believed in her dream.

****

Rebecca is seasick, and her body aches from heaving. Her back throbs with each lurch along the gunwale of the bark, finally losing her grip on the belaying pins amidships. Bitter fear fills her mouth. She faces the howling night, wondering what terrors may come from her waking dream. Black planks shine greasy with spray, blood, and vomit. Wind shears through the rigging above, then sweeps the deck, carrying Rebecca farther aft. I can see her very close. Entering this dream, I become her, shivering with the lifeless cold of the nor'easter: the Devil's breath of the north Atlantic.

I fly to the gunwale, again, as the ship yaws hard to port. The deck rises to snatch me. The sea turns ghost-white with foam. The tremendous weight of the ship—180 tons—hits my legs like that of the whole Earth exploding. I fall. There's nothing to hold onto as the keel strikes the edge of the reef. The beam cracks completely, sending a shudder up the masts and down along the planks. Torn sailcloth pops and flutters in the squall as if it were a doily, while the stern rises impossibly high. The prow rams the spine of the Earth exposed below the shallow tide pool.

In the blinding storm, we have drifted close to land—close enough to die. Yet, instead of backing away, we drive farther onto the rocks. The ship has become a maddened lover pressing the subject of its desire, raping Mother Earth in an act of lust and self-destruction. We won't be returning to Belton in this lifetime or on this ship. With each desperate lunge, wood splinters with a hideous boom and the groaning of timbers.

I reach for the end of a rope, only to have it slither away. Soon the main mast shatters. There's no time to seek the boats. I'm thrown into the surging sea, so close to land but in the blackness of the storm, the shore is like the unfathomable depths. I try to swim, but it's no use. The sound of the dying ship bellows back at the sky.

A swell lifts me off the rocks to deeper water, pulling toward a line of breakers dimly visible through the rain. I'm too sick to be afraid and too weary to fight the waves that hasten toward the shore.

Topsy-turvy, I plummet and land hard against the roof of the sky. Pebbles and shells scuttle away with a scratching rush of clouds—a clacking sound like a sigh. Drowning in the spray and surf, I dare not breathe. Blindly, I reach down toward the land and feel nothing but sky. I'm hurtling as the waves close in. My hand pounds like rocks falling, like logs jammed in a river, like horses' hooves along the hard-packed highway to Staffordshire. It is the echoing sound of loneliness.

For a lifetime, I'm carried by the undulation of this unseen power. Is it God? I do not know, but I smell the mystery of its essence in the sour, salt-soaked mist exhaled by the moaning sea. Again my head slams against the ceiling of the sky as I tumble and fall. A great magnet holds me there as waves lick hungrily at my legs and arms, pulling me back to the destruction of the ship as if to England, home no more.

Before unconsciousness overtakes me, I hear the twittering of wrens and swallows along the marsh road I left two months before. I dig my hands into the cold gritty firmament. Here on this unknown shore, I lay my cheek against the outer wall of heaven and wait patiently for the calling of my name.

Instead of His sweet voice, I hear the screams of dying men. There is much cursing and the awesome din of battle. I hear the thud and clunk of heavy oars against the sides of long boats. So there were boats; then some may be saved—dear Father, let them be saved and with their salvation, may I be delivered as well. But my hope fades as my prayer is answered by paralyzing agony. I can make no sense of what is happening. I remember running, then falling, crawling and running—hurtling into lightless depths.

****

When I open my eyes, I see not the pale beach or the black, rocky shore, but the greens and browns of a forest. Somewhere far beneath me, I feel my legs. I lean back against a massive beechnut tree, its trunk the color of an elephant's hide, its garnet leaves rustling wetly in a gentle wind. The sunny sky is feathered with these hideous tournament banners—great leafy trophies of some regal and deadly game of sport. Dreamily, at first, I look at my side drawn by a distant pain that tears with a serpent's fangs at my consciousness. What I see sends nausea surging through my frame. There's a ragged hole in my bodice as if some wild beast has bitten through the cloth and stays. How much more easily it desecrated my chemise. But, dear God, its vicious attack did not stop there. To my horror, I see my flesh torn from my ribs and below, exposing in its gore the inner workings of my body, like the unhinged back of a grandfather clock. Instinctively, I cover the hole with my bloodied hand and sink into a hollow in the great tree that is as deep as the entrance to a secret grotto or a grave. Before the portal to dreamless sleep, I repeat one bewildering question: Why?

****

Only hours earlier, a band of the King's infantry advances in close quarter along an unnamed beach in an unknown world. Their formation moves under moonlight as if the shadow of a cloud below the slackening wind. They hold to the crest of the high water line, near rhododendron boughs reaching from the bluff. The five men move mechanically, as if in fear. Sweat and blood glisten on their forearms and naked breasts and across their faces and necks.

Three of the men carry long pikes that they thrust into the night. Another grips a broadsword. The fifth man cradles a newly fabricated dog-lock musket.

The soldiers freeze momentarily, as if stricken by lightning. They press inward, forming a solid wall, their chests heaving. The swordsman retires to the rear, while the musketeer advances. He sights along the smooth of the barrel at a shape rising near the water's edge.

"The devil's coming from the sea to cut our throats," mutters one of the pikemen, a 34-year-old debtor from Sussex.

"Steady, Sergeant Pickworth," commands Captain Heathe.

"Forsaking the treachery of the savage bastards that ambushed us, I want him to know his Master before he dies. The ball shall tear open his profane breast to release the fires of Hell from where his Christian soul should be. God be with us, lads. Stand ready to receive the Horseman. Look lively now. The beast approaches fast."

The men grind their heels into the sea-soaked sand. Their pikes aim at the thousand eyes of an unseen enemy. The musketeer sucks in a salty breath and lets it out. Then he draws another reverently, as if it is his last, and holds it against the pressure of his finger on the trigger of his musket. He must care not for the heavy recoil of the explosion. He looks only headlong toward the coming of the Apocalypse. The man-beast seems to hesitate, then lunges forward. A high-pitched scream crests from the crashing waves drawn from a guttural moan.

"Make ready!" shouts Captain Heathe.

Upon this command, the musketeer brings his piece to full cock with a metallic click, unnatural and final.

"Present!" commands his captain.

All becomes stillness except for a shadow looming from the edge of the sea.

"Fire!"

The blast sends a torch blazing along the beach. A plume of smoke billows after, carrying away all sight of the enemy.

****

Still dizzy from the pinwheel bucking of the universe, Rebecca leans away from the sea into the gravity of the rising beach. She begins to fall when the wind shifts and becomes momentarily still. Then a singing rush of sound careens toward her: the hissing of a giant snake. The fangs of the musket ball bite deeply, knocking her to the sand. Its jaws rip open her side with a burning she does not believe possible. She begins to crawl and then in fear she stands to confront the fire. Somehow, she runs toward the edge of rhododendron, seeking a place to hide. From far away in time, she hears men shouting, drowned by a crescendo of horses' hooves pounding down the old highway toward Staffordshire, leaving Belton forever.

****

"Tell me, Ma, tell me, again about Rebecca," pleaded Magellan.

Ethel Crowne Burns stood at the soapstone sink and looked out the kitchen window—beyond the apple orchard. Magellan could almost see her mother's mind move back one century at a time—long before the cow pasture and the dusty green of the woods. Her hands didn't cease snapping beans and rinsing them in the bucket of cool water. Magellan watched the back of her neck and her slow breathing.

"Lordy, girl, I must've told you that story a thousand times over the past seventeen years. I'd think you'd know it by heart and could tell it to yourself."

"I do, Ma, and I will, I just like the way you tell it. I'm writing it down, and I want to get it right."

"Writing it down? You mean like a school paper?"

Magellan hesitated. "It's a special paper, Ma, a chapter in my journal. I'm reading it at graduation, and it's about American history."

"That's your history. I don't know about any American history."

"It's special, Ma, and this chapter will be sort of a speech. Mr. Samuals asked me. He recommended me to Mr. Creighly, the principal."

"I don't like that Samuals."

"Ma, you don't know him."

"Better than that. I know his Ma and Pa. I went to school with his Pa. He was a no-account and Lucy Jackson was trash from down off the Point. Nothing good could've come from them gett'n' together."

"Ma, he's very nice, and he's brilliant." She lowered her eyes, cautious of her enthusiasm. "He really likes my writing. He says I have a real talent for telling a story."

Mrs. Burns hadn't drawn her eyes back from the darkness of the woods all during their argument. She held her head fixed, and she peered at the distance as if willing the past to remain where it was. "Dead and buried," she said. "And good riddance to boot. Where is telling a story going to get you in this world, Magellan! Answer me that. Lordy knows I love you, girl. But what happiness is there goin' to be in this dreaming? It's quite enough your Pa let you finish high school. For all that'll bring you is heartache. At least you learned to type and sew a hem, although not a very straight one from what I've seen."

"Typing will help me in my writing, Ma. If I only had a Smith Corona like the ones in Miss Pennerton's class." Magellan glanced wistfully at her mother who appeared no longer to be paying attention to her, so fixed her gaze seemed at something reflected out the window.

"It's a good skill for a woman. Without a skill, you're nothing more than a streetwalker and Lordy knows there's enough competition in that line on Benefit Street in Providence and in Little Italy on the Hill." She paused, "And right down on the Point, here in Drownville. You got to keep your pride, Magellan. You got to maintain your Pa's name, my name. Remember who you are. You're a Crowne."

"Pa's a Burns, Ma," Magellan corrected her mother. She quickly regretted her impulse, seeing her mother's back tighten and the back of her steel-gray head rise and begin to turn.

"I know, but I'm a Crowne, and in this town, that's what matters. Your Pa married into the Crownes and that's your birthright even if there ain't any money behind it. Not on our side, anyway. But a Crowne's a Crowne and that's something to be proud of."

"Rebecca was a Crowne," Magellan said, bringing the conversation back to her original question.

Mrs. Burns now looked at her daughter.

"Writing. You're always poking in that journal of yours. And dreaming. No child of mine is going to be a writer. That's almost as bad as a stage actor or a dance-hall singer. Floozies. That's what they are."

"Ma," was Magellan's only protest.

"Floozies. I won't stand for you getting up there in front of the whole town and shaming your great, great, great grandmamma. It wouldn't be right."

"Ma, I'm proud of Rebecca. And you said yourself she was a Crowne. The whole town will be proud of how she survived."

"Survived. I'll suffer you that. But some would say she should've let herself die before she let those savages touch her, a Christian woman and never been with a man. You would have thought no white man would want her after what she'd done."

"But Joel did want her and if he hadn't, we wouldn't be here, would we?" Magellan knew this was thin ice, and heard the sudden cracking of the firmament of her dreams.

"I suppose not. But who'd have known the difference? It's about appearances, isn't it? It's about perceptions and opinions that count in this town—in this world. What she did? Living with those heathens. Let them do God-knows-what to her. Listen here, Missy. You get that idea out of your head right now."

"Ma, I want you and Pa to be proud of me. I'm proud of our heritage. I'm going to read this chapter at graduation and you'll be proud of me, too. I know you will."

"No, I won't."

"Why not, Ma?" There was a hitch in her voice, and the words caught somewhere as if wanting to hold it all back, stop the conversation from where it was going, bring back the hope. But the water spilled over the top of the dam, and her mother's words came rushing now, drowning her, washing away the dream.

"Because I won't be there. That's why. It's a waste of my time just like this schooling is a waste of your time and foolish dreaming. What you need is a job, Missy, a good secretarial job. In case you hadn't heard, there's still a Depression pressing on us."

Magellan sat with her back straight, as Miss Pennerton had taught her. She pretended she was only facing a typewriter, fitted routinely with a blank sheet. But unlike the machine she'd deftly learned to manipulate, her mother's will remained inscrutable. Ethel Crowne Burns was steadfast in her beliefs, perhaps even stubborn—by her own proud admission cut from old New England stock. This was a legacy as solid as the granite coast of Aquidneck Island, yet to her daughter, as fathomless as Rhode Island's broad Narragansett Bay.

****

Later that night, Magellan looked at her pencil lying in the groove carved in the old clerk's table. Inspired, she picked it up and wrote, "My life has always been like a flood tide on the Kickemuit River, sweet salt air carried inland with the rising sea, whispering through the eel grass."

Disgusted, she put down the pencil and spoke to the shadows. "I can't write that. That's like Walt Whitman. Copying is what it is. I can't write at all."

Magellan crossed out the line, leaned against the spines of the Windsor chair, and tried to look beyond the shadowed walls of the room to the forest above the inlet in her mind. She began to feel the cool, hard bark of Rebecca's beechnut tree. Such thoughts began to pull at her hands, flowing and ebbing. Again, she laid down her pencil. Holding the small lined tablet, she reread lines she'd written earlier.

"This isn't right," she said softly so the shadows wouldn't hear. "This isn't how it was at all."

Magellan's thoughts sped past graduation toward summer. In four weeks, her family would move to the summer cottage on the Kickemuit River, outside the Town of Warren, Rhode Island, just across the bridge from Drownville. She loved summers more than anything. But this one was special—her graduation summer. She'd have her diploma. She was a woman, complete and powerful with an unspoken promise. She thought about Rebecca, how desperate she must've felt that night.

****

Rebecca doesn't feel the passage of time. Her focus centers on the pain that holds her as a bodice of fire, consuming her. Her consciousness spins out of control. She falls into her shadow—the hollowed-out tree seems a lonely place to hide—deep as the expanse of the sea or the dream of tomorrow.

Perhaps, she has never left the ship, and she's dreaming as she drowns. Her life dissolves around her. Here is blessed darkness that takes away all pain, a comfort that must be the embrace of the Almighty or the touch of His beloved Son.

The hand that caresses her hair and face must be Holy. She sees a picture of Jesus reaching out to her, his long hair flowing across his shoulders. But something is wrong. Jesus wears no beard upon his face. His features are dark but proud and serene. His upper body is naked. Dear God, can this be? She's confused. Rebecca sees flesh in the firelight that flickers around His halo as if she's lying on a funeral pyre—the Apocalypse surely, but how can she explain His nakedness?

She closes her eyes, unable to understand this intimacy of her union with her Lord. What can this mean? Who can she tell? Then dark waves surge over her—pain, such pain—carrying her in its flood tide, rhythmical and absolute.

Freak Potential
By Bob Strother

I wander among the shelves
Sipping decaf from my
One-hundred-percent–
Recycled paper cup.

Book-club ladies chat
Earnestly in a circle,
Spectacles on neck-chains,
All blue hair and cat sweaters.

Sweet sixteen sits cross-legged
On the floor, black fingernails,
Tattooed tears dripping
From her cheeks.

Nose-ringed counter help
Ring my purchases then
Twitter their friends, I'm
Sure, about me.

B&N, mainstream America.
Face-metal, Facebook,
Face the music.
What am I?

THIS FACILITY
CLOSED
BECAUSE OF PUBLIC
ABUSE AND VANDALISM

Ships in the Night
By Charles P. Reeve

Nobody would want a daddy like mine. I've never been good enough for him, and I'm tired of being a punching bag. For years, he's threatened to throw me out of the house on my 18th birthday, which is tomorrow. Well, I'm not giving him the pleasure. Earlier, I snuck into his bedroom closet and stole his favorite pistol. He didn't notice. He was busy watching a Seahawks game.

Daddy beats Mama, too, when he's drunk. Mama and I have thought about killing him, but we don't like the idea of going to jail. Do they beat you in jail? Mama's too scared to fight back. She's always tried to protect me, though, so I know she loves me. I grab a pen and paper.

Mama and Daddy, I'm leaving for good tonight. Don't bother looking for me. I'll probably be dead. I have no future, and I'm tired of living in hell. Judith. I fold the note and slip a corner under my dresser lamp. After grimacing at the image in the mirror, I pull my dirty-blond hair into a ponytail and grab my backpack. I open the window and step into the cool August night.

As I trudge out the long, gravel driveway, the flickering light from the living room grows dimmer. I reach Highway 101 and look to the right toward Bruceport and South Bend. City lights add a faint glow to the distant sky. I turn left toward the star-spangled blackness, and feel my way along the shoulder of the road. Maybe I'll hitch a ride to California and lose myself on a crowded beach. Maybe not.

In a couple of minutes, a car roars past with a pickup truck on its tail. The pickup passes and disappears into the night. I stumble along a few more minutes. It's easy to lose track of time under the stars. I gaze upward and wonder if planets circle those points of light. I wonder if people live there, and if they treat their children better than Earthlings do.

Another car whizzes past. Its brake lights flash on, and it pulls off the road. *Who would stop for a hitchhiker at ten o'clock at night in the Washington countryside? Two to one it's a pervert.* I stride across the road and approach the driver's door. The window rolls down and I see a well-groomed man dimly lit by red panel lights. He seems to be alone.

"Hello there," he says in a too-cheerful voice. "Do you need a lift?"

He looks like an OK guy, but you never know. "Yeah, I guess so."

"Where are you headed?"

"Down the coast—maybe to Oregon or California."

"I'm headed toward Portland, but I can't promise how far I'll go tonight. I could use some company." He pushes a button and the doors unlock. I walk behind the car and see a Washington license plate. I slip out of the backpack and take a seat in the front.

"Buckle up," he says.

I snap the harness into place and adjust the backpack on my lap. Through the canvas, I stroke the cold, hard barrel of the gun with my left hand. Out of the corner of my eye, I see him sizing me up. *If he tries anything, I'll shoot him.* I turn the backpack halfway around. I'm right-handed.

He pulls back onto the road and accelerates. "We may as well introduce ourselves," he says. "My name is Hugh." He offers his right hand, which I ignore.

"My name's Judith," I say. "My mother calls me Judy, and my father calls me Judo."

"What would you like *me* to call you?"

"Any friggin' thing but Judo."

"All right, it's Judith, then. So, are you headed back to college?"

"What gives you that idea?"

"Isn't that an Oregon State jersey you're wearing?"

"My boyfriend gave it to me. I barely survived high school."

"Then you must be about eighteen?"

Geez, the guy wants it legal. How considerate. I wonder if he likes fat girls. "I'll be eighteen on eight eighteen—just a couple of hours from now. How about yourself, Hugh?"

He chuckles. "I've lost count. Maybe forty-two or so." *Good grief, old enough to be my father.* "Judith, I'm curious about the girls of your generation. What's with the body piercings and tattoos?"

"It's no big deal."

"But why would a girl disfigure herself? Tattoos go with you to the grave, you know."

"So?"

"Do you have any?"

"Just a small one near my belly button—a red rosebud. Want to see?"

Hugh glances in the rearview mirror. "Not really. Why did you do it?"

"Probably a combination of things: rebellion, peer pressure, curiosity. I don't expect to make it to twenty, though, so what's the big deal?"

"Does your father know about the rosebud?"

"I've managed to hide it."

Hugh pauses a moment to choose his next words. "Are you all right?" he says. "I mean, are you sick or anything?"

"Why?"

"Well, your voice sounds so lifeless, so void of emotion."

"So why do you care?"

"Curiosity, I guess. I like to meet new people and learn about them." He eyeballs me again, which I try to ignore. "You have an interesting face, Judith. Your bone structure is rather elegant. All you need is a little more meat on those bones."

Oh, brother, pickup line number 73. I trace the outline of the gun with my right forefinger. *Should I kill us both or just myself?* "What do you mean, *more meat*?"

"You're rather skinny, don't you think?"

"Skinny? Are you nuts, mister?"

"Please, call me Hugh."

"If I'm skinny, Hugh, how come I see a fat girl every time I look in a mirror? My belly bulges out like a water balloon."

"How tall are you?"

"Five-seven. Why do you care?" *Do you like the tall, fat type?*

"Humor me. How much do you weigh?"

"A hundred and six."

"Do you call that fat?"

"I'd rather be under a hundred."

"Oh, I see," he says. "Anorexia? Bulimia?"

"What? You think I like to puke or something?"

"Then you starve yourself. What have you eaten today?"

"Mr. Hugh, is this something you really need to know?"

"Just plain Hugh, please. No, I don't *need* to know, but I'd *like* to know. You interest me."

"OK, I had a glass of orange juice for breakfast, and a piece of lettuce and half a carrot for lunch. Oh, yeah, and I ate a chunk of potato out of Mama's homemade beef stew. Now are you satisfied?"

"You must be starving. Why don't we stop at the next diner?"

"I'm *not* hungry." *How's that for void of emotion?*

"How long have you been like this?"

"A long time, and *yes*, I've talked to counselors about it, and *yes*, it's called anorexia, and *yes* it does have something to do with my father."

"Your father, huh?"

I'm feeling anxious now, so I reach into a small zippered pocket and pull out a bottle of diet pills. I toss two into my throat and swallow.

"What kind of pills are those?" he says.

"Diet."

"Do they keep you from getting hungry?"

"Yeah, and they make me feel better."

"I see. Now tell me about your father."

"OK, if you insist. My father is the most *evil* person I've ever known. He's spent eighteen years making my life miserable. If it weren't for Mama, he would have killed me by now.

"How does he make you miserable?"

What? You need ideas on how to abuse me? "Well, for starters he constantly criticizes me, calls me every curse word in the book, and hits me when he's drunk. I could show you bruises."

"Not necessary. Go on."

"He wanted a son, so he lets me know that I don't fill the bill. He makes me do heavy yard work that *he* ought to be doing. He likes to scare me and then laugh about it. He makes fun of my boyish figure. Hell, he's the world's biggest hypocrite. The people at his car dealership think he's Mr. Nice Guy. If they only knew."

"I'm sorry it's been so bad for you, Judith. That's enough to mess up any girl."

"He's done other stuff, too, like the time he caught my boyfriend, Kenny, in my bedroom. That's when he started calling me a little whore. We were just talking. Kenny escaped through the window, but my backside sure didn't. I don't want to talk about it anymore."

"I understand," he says. "How does he treat your mother?"

"He hits her when he's drunk. I've seen the bruises."

Hugh pats my left knee. "I know all of this is painful, honey, so I won't press you for any more details." *Honey? How touching!* He's quiet for a minute and then says, "Do you really think that a hundred pounds is a healthy weight for you?"

"If I'm any heavier, I look fat. I don't want to look fat!"

"Hold out your left hand, please."

"Why?"

"Hold it out for a moment. I want to check something."

I see oncoming headlights. "OK, but wait 'til that car passes. No use causing a wreck. By the way, this car seems pretty classy. What kind is it?"

"A Lexus. I hope that's not what your father sells."

I laugh for the first time tonight. "I don't think so." The car roars past, and then it's dark again. The darkness provides an unexpected comfort. I hold out my left hand, and Hugh circles his thumb and forefinger around my wrist.

"You have a medium bone structure. I'd say that one forty is a healthy weight for a girl your height. You could have a lot of fun putting on thirty-four pounds."

"I told you I don't like to eat. I'm fine the way I am."

"You may feel that way now, but your insides are hurting in a way that they can't communicate. I'm not a doctor, but I've studied some physiology and psychology. I don't expect you to run out and eat a double cheeseburger tonight. All I ask is that you listen to what I say, and believe that I care."

Oh, God, here he goes endearing himself again. The moves can't be far behind. Why should he care about me? He's known me for less than half an hour. Who's he kidding? It's beginning to look spooky out there—trees thick on both sides of the road. We must be getting close to Oregon. I stroke the gun barrel again.

For the next minute, the only sound is the humming of tires on pavement. Periodically, we pass a break in the trees and see the great blackness of the Pacific Ocean. A fat moon hovers above the hills to the east. Hugh breaks the silence with words that startle me.

"I'm afraid I misled you earlier, Judith. We're not driving all the way to Portland."

"Then where?"

"We'll be turning onto a dirt road in another mile or two. I'm meeting a friend there."

Oh, great, a gang-bang in the middle of nowhere. God help me. For a split second, I wish I were back home, even with Daddy in the house. *No, come to think of it, I don't.* "So what about me, or don't I want to know?"

Hugh laughs. "You won't be harmed. I don't have any further use for this car, so it's yours, free and clear."

"What? You're kidding, right?"

"I'm quite serious. You *do* know how to drive, don't you?"

"Of course." Strangely, I feel a twinge of disappointment. His attention has been nice. We turn inland on a dirt road and meander through the dense woods for a while. Hugh pulls to a stop in a small clearing and turns the car around. The sweep of headlights reveals only trees and dense undergrowth. "You sure meet people in strange places," I say.

"There's a reason for it. My work requires secrecy. I'll go on foot the rest of the way. You're free to leave. Enjoy the car." He opens the door and steps out. I slide behind the wheel and search for the gearshift. He offers his hand, and we part with a handshake.

"Good luck, Judith," he says

"Thanks, Hugh. Same to you." He strides quickly to the rear and disappears from the reach of the taillights. I'm alone again. *Is this what they mean by ships passing in the night?* I shift into drive and roll maybe 50 yards before stopping. I snap off the headlights and cut the engine. Blackness envelops the car, which seems colder. For a moment, I feel lost in the universe. *Is this what death is like? Still?*

Quiet? Dark? It starts to feel friendly again. I glance in the rearview mirror and see a blue flash. Jerking my head around, I see only blackness.

I start the engine, switch on the headlights, and follow the beams to 101. I waver a moment and then turn left. Feeling empty, I begin to sob. Tears fill my eyes, and the road gets blurry. I pull over at the first opportunity—a scenic overlook. I park the car next to a railing, grab my backpack, and open the door. The air feels cool and still. The moonlit surf crashes onto jagged rocks below in a brain-filling roar. I climb onto the hood and lean back against the windshield. The warmth of the engine feels good on my backside.

I unzip a pocket of the backpack and pull out the pistol. It feels cold and hard in my hands. *Daddy, you'll have to find someone else to torture. I've had enough.* I point the barrel at my right ear. *In the movies, they usually stick it in their mouth, but I don't want my last thought on Earth to be the metallic taste of the damned barrel.* I close my eyes, and a blackness darker than the forest fills me. I squeeze the trigger and barely hear a click.

My head collapses against the windshield, and stars swirl before my eyes. *Is this heaven or hell?* In a moment, I realize that I'm still alive. *Was the bullet a dud or a blank?* I point to my ear and squeeze again. Nothing. I point toward the stars and squeeze. Again, I hear nothing. It's not like Daddy to keep a gun unloaded. I withdraw the clip and look at the bullets. In the moonlight, they look real. I toss the pistol and clip into the weeds.

Wait a minute! Don't blanks have wadding? I've heard of people being killed by the concussion of wadding. No, these bullets were duds, but why? Is this Daddy's way of tormenting me further? Well, it won't work, Daddy. I will control my destiny, not you—I, I, I. Let's see you stop this. I strap on my backpack, slide off the hood, climb over the railing, make a mad dash, and plunge over the cliff toward the foaming rocks. *Will it hurt to die this way?*

Suddenly, a blue light blinds me. My senses go numb, and then I'm sitting in a stuffed chair in a dimly lit room. *Is this the judgment chamber?* My backpack is uncomfortable, so I take it off and drop it on the floor. Across a metallic table are three similar chairs pointed in my direction. In the middle one is a man's figure. My eyes adjust, and I see that it looks like Hugh, except that he's wearing a gray uniform.

"I was hoping that it wouldn't come to this, Judith."

It's Hugh's voice. I'm sure of it. "Hugh, is that you?"

"Yes."

"Where are we?"

"This is my reception room. So, you tried to kill yourself, did you?"

"About three times, I think."

"I suspected you might try, but I thought that when the bullets failed you might take it as a sign that you were meant to live."

"Are you saying that *you* had something to do with those bullets not firing?"

"I did."

"But how?"

"I confess to having certain powers that I've concealed from you. I simply changed the molecular structure of the powder in the bullets, but when you dived off the cliff, well, I had to take drastic action." Hugh pulls a pistol out of his pocket and lays it on the table.

"That's Daddy's pistol," I say.

"It's an expensive weapon, a Glock .40 caliber semi-automatic. I imagine he'll be upset to find it missing."

"So who cares?"

"Would you like to return it?"

"No way."

"Then I'll keep it as a souvenir."

"Be my guest. So what happens now, Hugh? Is Hugh your real name?"

"Yes, it is."

"Are you from outer space?"

He ignores my question and motions with his right hand. A younger man steps out of the shadows. Hugh whispers in his ear, and the man leaves.

"Now, what were you asking?" he says. "Oh yes, am I from outer space? The truth is, I come from a civilization that's advanced far beyond yours, both socially and technologically. I'm assigned to walk among you to study your culture. It's for a benevolent purpose, I assure you."

"So, is this your spaceship?"

"It gets me where I need to go. Say, could I see that bottle of pills?"

"Why?"

"Humor me, please."

I unzip the small pocket, pull out the bottle, and toss it to Hugh, who snags it with his left hand. He presses a button on the table, and a hole opens. He drops the bottle into it.

"Do you have any other drugs or alcohol?"

"No."

"Good. I'm glad you're being truthful."

"Oh, I get it. You're testing me. If you can change the powder in the bullets, then you probably know what's in my backpack."

Hugh smiles. "An excellent deduction. You won't be needing those pills any longer."

"Why? Am I going to die tonight?"

"No, you're going to start living."

"I already *am* living—that's the whole problem."

"You're *surviving*, to be sure, but I want you to start *living* again."

"It's a nice thought, but you'd better come up with another miracle or two."

"Very well," says Hugh with a wave of his hand. The young man reappears with a glass of liquid, which he sets in front of me. "Judith, this my assistant, Manley."

"Hello, Miss Judith," says Manley.

"Hello."

Hugh motions for Manley to leave and then says, "He brings refreshment. It tastes like a lemon shake. I urge you to drink it."

"I'm not hungry *or* thirsty."

"Judith, you *must* trust me on this. There are problems lurking down the road due to your anorexia. Some of them will not appear for another twenty or thirty years. This one drink, a mere six ounces, will alleviate those problems and restore your appetite. You need do nothing more than eat a reasonably balanced diet and aim for that one-forty mark. I'm offering you a second chance. What happens next is entirely up to you."

"Should I go home or keep heading south?"

"Whichever you choose."

"I guess I ought to go home, but what about Daddy?"

"You're stronger now. He won't hurt you again."

"Is the car still mine? Is that how I get back home, or do you beam me down into my bedroom?"

Hugh chuckles. "The car is yours. I'll return you to it soon. If you check the registration in the glove box, you'll see your name listed as the owner. Drive carefully and enjoy it. Now, drink up."

My right hand reaches for the glass, and I sip its contents. I like the taste. The liquid slides down my throat, and my insides begin to tingle.

Hugh notices my reaction and says, "The sensations will diminish over the next hour."

I fidget with the empty glass and examine the shapes cut into it.

"Beautiful, isn't it?" he says. "It's made of the finest crystal." I gently set the glass on the table. Manley reenters and whispers in Hugh's ear. Hugh nods and says, "It's time for you to go, Judith. Take hold of your backpack and stay seated. In a moment, you'll be back at your car. This time, no diving off the cliff, please."

I laugh. *How long has it been since I laughed with joy?* Hugh walks over and clamps my right hand between both of his. The warmth in his hands matches the warmth of his spirit.

"I like you, Hugh," I confess. "Will I ever see you again?"

"It's possible, but that's not important. What *is* important is that you choose to live—*dare* to live." Hugh walks back to his chair and reaches for a lever. "Farewell, Miss Judith."

My throat is tight. I choke out, "Farewell."

A blue light envelops me, and the next thing I know, I'm sitting on the hood of the Lexus. The moon is higher in the sky, its silver beams washing out the stains of the world. With a newfound strength, I hop off the hood, yank open the door, and toss my backpack onto the front seat. I cast a final look across the thundering ocean as a shooting star flashes toward the horizon.

I don't remember much about the ride back to Bruceport. Between the racing of my mind and the tingling in my stomach, I'm lucky that I was able to stay on the road. When I turn into our driveway, I hear the familiar sound of gravel crunching under the tires. The flashing lights of an ambulance catch my eye. *Oh, God, is it mother?*

I park the Lexus in the side yard and run up to the ambulance. A body lies on a stretcher inside, a cloth pulled over its head. An attendant is securing the stretcher with straps.

"I'm the daughter," I say. "Which one is it?"

Before he can answer, a voice shrieks my name. Mama dashes out the front door and down the sidewalk. We embrace as never before.

"Where have you been, Judy?" she cries.

"I'll tell you later, Mama. What happened to Daddy?"

"I was spreading frosting on your birthday cake when he yelled to bring him another beer. I said, 'Just a minute, my hands are sticky.' I washed up and grabbed a beer from the refrigerator. When I got to him, he was slumped over in his chair. He wasn't breathing, so I called an ambulance."

"Do they know what happened?"

"Probably a heart attack. They said there's no way I could have saved him."

I turn and watch the ambulance lights disappear down the driveway. Words of encouragement pop into my head. "He's gone now, Mama, and we're free. We can pull ourselves up and begin to live the way people *should* live. His death is a gift we must honor. The misery of the past is over."

"The paramedics said they would do an autopsy."

"Don't worry, Mama. They won't find a thing inside that man except rotten filth. Come on inside now."

Mama and I walk arm in arm to the door.

"Your birthday cake is almost ready," she says. "I need to finish icing it."

"While you're doing that, I'll grab my backpack and put my stuff away. Is there any of your homemade beef stew left? I'm hungry."

Tears come to Mama's eyes. "Oh, sweetie, I'll heat you up some right away. The icing can wait."

Mama dances toward the kitchen. It's been ages since I've heard joy in her voice.

As I toss the backpack onto my bed, a glint from the dresser catches my eye. An empty crystal glass sits on top of my farewell note. I walk to the dresser, lift the glass, and unfold the note. A large red "X" covers my words, and written below them—in red ink and perfect script—are the words, "Happy Birth Day, Judith. Always, Hugh."

Tyrants
By Tim Harkins

John drunk-dialed Idi Amin.
It was the Seventies. He couldn't
just Google the palace number.
But John was an aspiring poet,
and the muse, a bottle of Wild Turkey,
assured John that Idi would benefit
from some insights into his questionable
family history. The overseas
operator didn't have the number,
nor did she think John was joking
(Ma Bell was a serious soul).
She connected him to a switchboard
somewhere in Uganda who connected
him to a cultured-sounding fellow
with a British accent who answered:
Command Post. And:
No, you cannot speak to His Excellency
President for Life. He hasn't risen yet.
In lieu of direct contact, John suggested
the aide tell the fat rat bastard, son-of-a-bitch
to execute himself half a million times.
John hated tyranny that much.
Next month, he hated his phone bill.

Sun Patch
By Brittany Vandeputte

A small square of light
In a dark room.
He sits neatly tucked,
All four paws inside.
His tail marks the boundary
Between light and shade.

Squirrel Friends
By Brittany Vandeputte

"Watch now. That squirrel is after your french fry." My grandfather leaned forward across the wooden picnic table and pointed at the bushy gray tail pulsing in the crook of an oak tree.

I dropped the fry I was holding to the ground, and with my toe, pushed it slowly across the dirt toward my new friend. Soon a furry blur ricocheted out of the tree, snatched the prize by my feet, and nibbled it from the safety of a nearby stand of trees.

"That's a rare treat for a squirrel," my grandfather said, licking his salty fingers.

"Why?" I asked, eying my cheeseburger and fries. "What do squirrels eat?"

My grandfather scanned the ground. His eyes lit on a small brown nut by the picnic-table leg. He plucked it between his thumb and forefinger. "They eat acorns," he said. "Like this."

I took it in my hand, and examined the smooth almost-wooden center, with the bumpy cap on top. "Fries probably taste better." I returned the acorn to his palm.

While I watched, he pried the acorn apart and held the little bowl between his two work-callused thumbs. He brought it to his lips and let out a short blast. "Back when I was your age," he said, "my grandfather taught me how to make an acorn whistle. Now I'm going to teach you."

\#

I took Sam to the park for the first time in February. It was the first day of the year that could be called warm, so we celebrated the almost-comfortable 50-degree weather with a picnic. We sat at a secluded table, the sun warming our shoulders, and enjoyed our meal of cheeseburgers and fries. A pair of squirrels started toward us. I pointed them out to Sam, all the while marveling at their bravery and wondering how much closer they'd dare to venture. I was more than surprised when they scampered right up to our picnic table and begged for french fries.

I sat there watching Sam watching the squirrels, and it reminded me of myself when I was two, learning about the natural world from my grandfather. Sam called the squirrels in the park his "squirrel friends," and it makes me happy that he thinks he has a relationship with them.

My grandfather died in 2005 and never had any "squirrel friends." Although he was an animal lover, my grandfather was also a hunter. On more than one occasion, I remember heaping plates of squirrel meat served at my grandparents' dinner table. It is understandable then that the squirrels in his neighborhood gave him a wide berth.

But across the street, the squirrels had found a safe haven. My grandfather's neighbor, Ira, had fed several generations of the same squirrel family for years. My grandfather and I would sit with Ira on his back porch cracking nuts for them and the squirrels would swarm us from every direction. Even my grandfather, the hunter, who once promised me a coat made out of their tails, delighted in the sight of happy chattering squirrels in our midst. Even at my very young age, I knew I was witnessing something extraordinarily uncommon.

Sitting on Ira's back porch, I decided that I wanted squirrel friends, too, and when I had children of my own, we would enjoy nature like my grandfather and I had, but we would feed the squirrels instead of hunt them.

#

"Look, Mommy! Here they come!" Sam and I returned to the park today, and while I unpacked our picnic, Sam climbed on top of the wooden picnic ta-

Sam looked down at the spread in front of him, and then his eyes returned to the squirrels clattering around the ground. "No fries?" he asked.

"No fries," I said. "Squirrels eat acorns."

My eyes scanned the ground for a small brown nut. "Like this."

Sam examined the almost-wooden center, with the bumpy cap on top. "I like fries." He returned his attention to his lunch.

ble and pointed in the direction of the woods. Soon our squirrel friends bounded toward us. They stopped short of the picnic table and buried their noses in a pile of dried leaves.

"They're eating lunch, too," I said, pulling the cheeseburger and fries from their cardboard-house container.

I pried the acorn apart and placed my thumbs over the acorn bowl, brought it to my lips, and let out a short blast.

"Back when I was your age," I said, "my grandfather taught me how to make an acorn whistle. Now I'm going to teach you."

Harley and the Mare
By Steve Heckman

A horse pissed on me today. I don't think she meant to. I mean, I'm sure she meant to pee. I just don't think it was personal.

Travis left the house early, for a Saturday. Big grin on his face. Didn't even give me a peck on the cheek. Shelly, our littlest, noticed.

"Mama, where's Daddy going in such a hurry, and with the trailer hooked up?"

That girl doesn't miss a thing. Travis says she's just like her Mama.

I tousled her hair. "I have a feeling we'll find out pretty soon."

Just before noon, I was pulling some weeds by the front-porch steps, and here he came back, flying up the gravel drive, tarp flapping over something in the trailer, leaning out the window, grin even bigger than when he left. When Travis puts a tarp over something, it's never good news.

The truck lurched to a stop next to me, and he leaned further out the window. "Guess what I got in back."

I stood up and slowly stretched. "Oh, let's see . . . a new dishwasher?"

He jumped out of the truck and fairly hopped to the back of the trailer. "Way better than that." He untied the tarp and yanked it part-way back.

"Oh, how sweet. You bought me an old motorcycle." Something about the battered bike looked familiar. The chrome was bright enough, but the paint on the gas tank was faded. It might have once been lime green, but now it just looked like a huge snot. There was a big metal bracket on one side, just below the tank.

Then I remembered. "Hey, isn't this old Norman Walker's bike?

"Yep. Seventy-Eight Harley V-twin. Ain't she sweet?"

Travis had a Harley back when we were dating. It may have been what hooked me on him. The sound of that thing was such a turn-on. I'd be on the back, arms clamped around that skinny waist, sitting at a stop light, and he'd goose it a couple of times. WUUMBAA, WUUMBAA. I'd liked to cream my jeans.

But that was a long time ago. Fortunately, Travis only broke one leg when he wrecked it. Never did get another bike.

Until now. Fourteen years and two kids later. Nothing much turned me on these days "Wait a minute. Didn't Norman's bike have a . . . ?"

Travis yanked back the rest of the tarp. "Sidecar. That's where Margie used to ride, even after she got sick. Then when she, uh, well anyway, without Margie to ride with anymore, Norman just parked it. Yesterday, he put a sign on it. Luckily I was driving by just as he put it out in the yard."

"Yeah, luckily."

"Took five hundred bucks for it. That's a steal."

"That's a dishwasher."

"Me and Tee Junior'll put her back together, and a little later, me and you'll go for a spin."

The sidecar, laying in the trailer with its half of the bracket sticking up in the air, same faded green paint as the gas tank, looked like an even bigger snot. "There's no way I'm riding in that thing. If I have to go along, I'll just sit on the back."

"I just figured you were too . . ."

"Fat?"

"Um, no."

"Well what, then?"

"I don't know why you always have to make everything so—complicated."

"OK, speaking of complicated, why didn't you just let me drive you over to Norman's and you could have ridden it home, instead of having to take it apart?"

"I wanted it to be a surprise. Anyway, it don't exactly, um, run."

"Oh, so I sit in the sidecar while you tinker with the carburetor? That's some surprise. I'm going in the house. Let me know when it's time for this 'spin.'"

"Send Tee Junior out while you're in there."

"If I can tear him away from *Grand Theft Auto*. I don't know why you buy him disgusting games like that."

"Aw, it's harmless. Anyway, he'll be driving in a couple of years, so it's good experience."

"Good ex . . . oh, never mind." I went into the house, let the door slam behind me. Tee Junior was already flying down the stairs—he must have seen the bike out the window.

Travis and Tee fiddled out there all afternoon, Travis cussing and sweating and drinking Icehouses, Junior laughing and running to the garage for tools and drinking sweet tea.

Then it happened. I was ironing and folding clothes while Shelly watched *Teletubbies*. Outside, that V-twin coughed once, barked a couple of times, then settled into a low rumble that made the water in the iron jiggle. Gave me a twinge. Travis goosed it a couple of times. WUUMBAA, WUUMBAA. That really did it.

Shelly looked up at me, eyes real big. "Mama, you OK?"

"Uh, yeah Shelly. Go get Mama a glass of water, OK, Honey?"

Shelly minced off to the kitchen. I was reaching under my shirt, dragging my bra around to where I could unhook it, fumbling and slipping it out of there. I undid the bottom few buttons of my shirt, tied it in a knot under my own V-twins, belly all just hanging out. I pulled the scrunchie out of my hair and gave my head a shake. I glanced in the mirror over the buffet. I looked good.

I had a pair of shorts right there in the hamper, but the stretch pants were staying on. The belly was one thing, but there was no way those thighs were seeing the light of day.

I was out the door and halfway down the porch steps, Shelley trailing behind spilling a glass of water, before Travis looked up. I stuck one arm up and turned a little pirouette at the bottom of the stairs.

Travis hopped off the Harley and danced a little jig. "Oh, yeah! Come on, my Harley Honey, we're going for a ride."

He hadn't called me that in a long time.

I looked down into the sidecar. Even out in the yard, it smelled musty, and it looked homemade. I glanced over at the bike, but it didn't have any backseat, just a big bicycle seat kind of thing for the driver. So the sidecar it was. If Margie, rest her soul, could do it, I could do it. I stepped in and struggled down into the seat. The wheel stuck up into the middle of it, right between my legs and about three inches from my crotch. The tire had exposed cords where the rubber had worn away.

I craned my neck back to look up at him. "Are you sure this thing's safe?"

He put his hands on his hips. "Now would I let you get in there if it wasn't safe?"

That made me feel a lot better. Not that it mattered, because he was already back on the bike, letting the clutch out, and we were moving.

I leaned back and hollered, "Tee, you keep an eye on Shelly now."

The last I saw them they were standing in the driveway, Shelly still holding the glass of water.

The sidecar rode like it didn't have any springs, and every tar strip in the road made me wish I had left that bra on, but pretty soon the blast of wind in my face made me forget my discomfort. I realized I didn't have on a helmet. Too late to worry about that. Anyway, it felt good to feel my hair streaming behind.

We rode up toward the mountains, waving to all the other motorcycles, and there were plenty of them out on a day like this. I remembered the downside of those glorious Harley pipes—after about 10 minutes of them blasting in my ear, I couldn't hear a thing. At a stop sign, I got Travis's attention and waved back toward the house. He looked disappointed, but he dutifully wheeled the ungainly contraption around in a wide circle and started back.

A couple miles from the house, we came up behind a trailer going really slow. As we got closer, I could see it was a horse trailer, two big brown asses inside, sticking up above the half-doors. I recognized them. They were the asses of our next-door neighbors' mares, Junie and Dribble, and we were going to be trapped behind them the rest of the way back to the house.

Except Travis had other ideas. He pulled up right behind the trailer and edged over to the double yellow line, leaning left, trying to look around the trailer to see if there was room to pass. We were so close all I could see was Dribble's swishing tail.

Then the tail stopped swishing and started raising up. Mashing a brake pedal that wasn't there, I tried to get Travis's attention, but he had downshifted to get ready for a pass, and the V-twin was roaring, and he was peering out around the trailer. The tail was way up now, and I could see the muscles in Dribble's thing working, and I hollered as loud as I could, but my holler was in the wind.

Then that piss, the one I mentioned before, started gushing out. You know what a mare's pee is like. It's no dribble or even a stream. It's more like a fire hose set on the wide pattern. It didn't take long for the first wave of it to travel the four feet from urethra to face, and I didn't have time to catch a breath after hollering. Trapped in that sidecar with no windshield and no helmet, all I could do was sit there and sputter under the deluge.

I swear Dribble was still peeing when Travis finally twisted the throttle and yanked the Harley across the double yellow. I was never so glad to see him make an illegal pass. He no sooner got back in our own lane than he started braking for our driveway.

The kids still stood there in the yard, and they stared at me as Travis jerked us to a stop by the porch steps. He followed their gaze.

"Well, look at you," he said. "What in the hell have you been doing?"

I didn't look at him. I was still spitting horse urine out of my mouth and trying to catch my breath. I heaved myself up out of the sidecar and stumbled, dripping, up onto the porch. "Tee, you turn around now, 'cause I'm not wearing these clothes into the house."

Half Full
By S. Jane Gari

If Rush Limbaugh doesn't shut up, you'll see me on the six o'clock news striding atop some lonely six-story with an AK-47 I borrowed from a redneck named Keith, who bought it for his daughter, took pictures of her with it and posted them on My Space. Keith once beat up a homeless man, emboldened by a twelve-pack of Bud, an aluminum bat, and rampant ignorance.
But if you need help at three in the morning—he'll ask no questions, give no excuses, and arrive at your doorstep at 3:15 with his sleeves rolled up.
Such are the world's birth pangs.
Be patient.

My father is unwavering in his worship of far-right pundits and practices the latest cut and paste e-mail scholarship that promulgates the worst madrasa-jihad-slander.
When my daughter stretched my belly, making a circus tent of my sundress, my father made jokes about large sea mammals and smuggled basketballs.
He assisted me down staircases gingerly, slowly, as if I were the only woman who had ever been pregnant in the history of the world.
My father cried silently in the corner of the hospital room when he saw that I was stuck at six centimeters for seven hours, when the doctor said my daughter was in stress and would have to be cut from me.
Such are the world's birth pangs.
Be patient.

Birth rips us asunder, places our insides in sterile trays and reconfigures them.
It hoists a screaming child above a blue drop cloth, like a bloody puppet, and asks you
to pledge your love
and sweat
and endless toil.
Such are the world's birth pangs.
Be patient.

Eight years ago, I was a teacher at Walt Whitman High School in New York where the students said "fag" and didn't know they were being taught on
the Old Fag's land;
they thought Walt was just some guy the local mall was named after.
When we finished the glorious poems in *Leaves of Grass* on Monday, September Tenth, one of the boys in my class cried and said he was sorry for saying "fag," and the next day he cried some more as he asked me if his father was dead while I closed the classroom windows to keep out the strange smell that we weren't told was metal and death until Thursday.
My friend's little brother, the fireman from Queens, fell catatonic because he collected teeth into one freakish pile for authorities to sift through and assign names.

My sister-in-law, who worked in Building Seven, had to see a shrink because she learned that if you stand on a sidewalk and watch people jump form the 90th floor, their bodies pop like balloons full of blood,
and she can tell you this at Thanksgiving with no expression on her face.

My husband, the helicopter pilot, will return from Katrina and Rita, shell-shocked from bloated bodies and the knowledge that his fellow countryman wanted to shoot him down,
and we will never live on the shore again,
although he proposed to me at a beach in New York.
Such are the world's birth pangs.
Be patient.

Because birth is painful,
Bloody,
Messy,
And miraculous.

So despite the mess, I still like to think the picture is a magnificent work of art—
That God,
whatever,
whoever,
is some great impressionist standing far enough away from the painting to see the grandeur.
And we can still get there
if we can just learn to stand far enough away,
Travel down some wormhole of a birth canal that blossoms open on the other end
Where we can view the painting through a newborn's telescope and say,
"Beautiful."

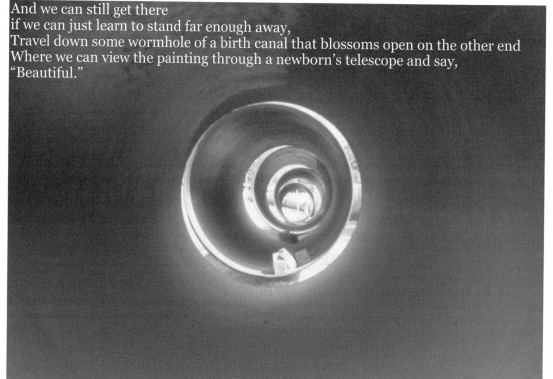

Strange Elvis Searches on Google
By Phil Arnold

Elvis Presley fans seem to be interested in every facet of his life, including some pretty obscure ones. So, what do these folks do to satisfy their curiosity? They Google it, of course. I have first-hand experience with this phenomenon as the host of a blog about Elvis. I started *ElvisBlog* four years ago, and since then, many thousands of Google searches have led people to my site.

In fact, *ElvisBlog* has become a favored source for many Elvis-related topics. Most are serious, but there are plenty of weird ones, too. I became aware of this when someone linked to my blog from a Google search for "Elvis pimples."

I can't imagine why anyone would even care about Elvis's pimples, but somebody did. My blog placed Number 2 on the Google list, beaten by a site with this news release: "National Pimple Center To Stage The Largest Charity Show In Singapore Next Year." Wow, who knew there was a National Pimple Center? One of the scheduled entertainers at that show was an Elvis Tribute Artist, so Google was merely connecting the two words "pimple" and "Elvis," even though they were not used together in the story. Dead end.

On the other hand, *ElvisBlog* had a legitimate reference to Elvis pimples. In a column entitled, "Never Before Told Elvis Secrets," I made fun of a 1977 *Midnight Globe* tabloid story that quoted Elvis's stepbrother Rick Stanley. One of his so-called revelations was this: "Until he was well into his 20s, Elvis had a terrible skin problem—just like a lot of young people. Pimples were his curse. He even had them on his back." I hope that information was of some value to the person who Googled.

From that point on, I saved other strange Elvis search topics on Google. It didn't take long until somebody searched for this: "Is Elvis's body preserved?" *ElvisBlog* could do no better than Number 8 on this one, but that's fine by me. Google simply found the words "body" and "Elvis" in the same article. However, *Elvis World-Japan* actually got into the topic. I was pleased with their quote, "Graceland CEO Jack Soden said there are no cryogenically *preserved* tissue samples of *Elvis*." But, then they went on to discuss other possible ways to clone Elvis. Oh, please, no! Please, pleeeeease, no!

A short while later, this one came up: "Diabetic Elvis impersonators." Why would anyone care? And Google couldn't find anything that covered the subject. However, the site at the top of their list had an article with an interesting title: "Calling all Elvis and Popeye Impersonators." I had to read that one to find out about Popeye impersonators.

The next one was like a trivia question, and I had no idea about the answer.

"Speedway, Viva Las Vegas and Easy Come, Easy Go, all have something in common what is it?" Was the person who Googled that trying to get the answer to a question that stumped her, or was she trying to stump Google? If the latter, it worked. None of the sites on the Google list gave the answer. They were there because they had seven or eight of the words somewhere in their contents. *ElvisBlog* had 10 of the words to rank Number 1.

Here is one I probably shouldn't mention, because it is not about a sandwich made of flies, as I originally thought. "Elvis fly sandwich" was actually about the Fool's Gold Sandwich, which Elvis *flew* from Memphis to Denver to get. Google got it right. The top of their list was a 2007 *ElvisBlog* article about this most unique Elvis story. The person who Googled this one didn't have to go anywhere else to get the information they wanted.

The next one made me laugh, until I saw how far down the list my blog was. Sadly, nine different websites beat out my blog on the Google results for: "Elvis Presley chest hair." This was just after I had posted a pictorial essay on Bare-Chested Elvis, with comments about his chest hair in one photo. Maybe it was too soon for Google to pick it up. Number 3 on the list was a site with an article entitled, "Did Tom Jones Insure His Chest Hair?" (According to that site, the answer is yes—for $25 million.)

The person who asked this one must have been a new fan not yet very familiar with Elvis's movies: "What Elvis and Ann-Margret movie was translated into Italian?" Well, let's see. There are so many Elvis and Ann-Margret movies, I'll just have to take a guess. How about *Viva Las Vegas*? Score another Number 1 for *ElvisBlog* with the 2008 article titled *Delinquente del Rock & Roll*, which covered the titles of all Elvis's movies on Italian DVDs. I knew about the Italian titles because they were on the back of a *Jailhouse Rock* DVD I bought in Rome while on vacation.

I was pretty sure the person who Googled this one wasn't going to find out the answer: "Three things Elvis did to nudge history along." He probably did more than three, but you'll have to look elsewhere to learn what they are. The Google list was jammed full of websites that had a reference to Elvis somewhere on their pages, plus the words history and nudge. Some of my favorite nudges were: Madonna nudging Elvis out of the top standing on the Billboard singles chart, Sam Phillips nudging Elvis along in the Sun recording studio, and radio stations nudging oldies formats off the air.

I just love this one: "Black midget Elvis." Apparently, there is no such thing. Many sites, including *ElvisBlog*, made reference to both Black Elvis and Midget Elvis, but apparently no enterprising black midget has tried to become an Elvis Tribute Artist. Will someone please step forward and fill this gaping void?

I have never seen a Google search topic longer than this: "Elvis impersonator movie where lady meets guy who looks like Elvis and she has a kid and she goes away with Elvis." My blog came up Number 1 on the results, but simply because it had used more of the key words in that long string than any other site did. It appeared that nothing Google found solved the mystery.

Someone had their facts a little off when they asked about a famous incident in Elvis history: "What color pants did Elvis split while recording 'Heartbreak Hotel'?" Or, perhaps this was another attempt to stump Google. If so, it worked. There was nothing on their list that led to an answer. The only time Elvis split his pants, he was performing, not recording. The song was "Poke Salad Annie," not "Heartbreak Hotel," and Elvis wore a jumpsuit when it happened on March 21, 1976, in Cincinnati.

Although this was covered in one of my articles, Google missed it. Instead, they found a number of search-topic words on my site, including bass player Bill Black's *split* from Elvis. I'll still take the Number 1 rank on their list, thank you.

We might as well end this story on a high note: "Elvis picking his nose." Not one choice on the Google list actually addressed this subject. They had references to Elvis, and nose, and picking, but fortunately picking always referred to a guitar. As I said at the beginning, Elvis fans seem interested in every facet of his life, but I think we'd be OK if we skipped this one.

It has occurred to me that some of the folks who did these weird searches and then linked to *ElvisBlog* may have become regular readers. That's a nice benefit. But, the big payoff came when my 11-year-old twin grandsons visited for the weekend. We sat around the computer and had fun. They were already well versed in using Google, so I told them, "Google 'Elvis pimples,'" and see how high Grampa Phil's blog comes up." When they saw it was Number 2, they laughed and thought that was so cool.

You should have seen the fun we had when they typed in "Elvis ripped his pants" and "Elvis picked his nose." Believe it or not, it seems my grandkids have now become Elvis fans. It's nice to have something to share with them.

A Moment of Silence
By Sally Arango Renata

There should be a moment of silence.
Rain should cease, plants stop growing,
waves pause, just for a moment

out of respect, for children pulled
from cement debris, lain on white sheets
to be named, mourned with a cross or altar.

There should be total quiet,
no movement, no rustle of leaves
not even the sound of river
washing rock.

Even flowers should close and crickets
stop to honor the thousands
pulled from mud,

those who will die from hunger, heat,
bugs born in squalid water. . .

If it were quiet, you'd hear a wail
escape the bellies of children, the bottled
scream
of mothers and fathers who bury part

of themselves. The sound would resound,
jar stars out of place, trees would fall,
the earth would crack open and the hearts of
all living things would pay homage.

The Country Road
By Lisa Wright-Dixon

It wasn't just any typical drive. This road had character. It plunged into a valley and then swooped up to a noble peak. Then it would freefall like a ride at the amusement park, dropping straight down, lifting riders out of their seats, leaving them with the feeling of "stomach in the mouth syndrome." It then leveled off into a plateau as if it meant to introduce each vehicle to the end of its ride. We were all drawn to its daring. Every teenager felt compelled to drag race their cars on the imperious road. It was a true test of guts and glory. Most times, we would land safely, ruining various parts of our parent's cars. Other times, the landings were not so safe. The road had its share of heroes and victims, tragic stories to tell.

Either way, no teen could resist the temptation of the road each time they journeyed to the local mall. During a drag race, the challenging car would pull alongside the opposing car while both traveled at high speed. It was the early 1970s, and girls were becoming accustomed to the women's rights movement. Feeling free, invincible, and just as equal to any boy, my girlfriends and I would pull up alongside a car full of them. Gunning the car engine gave the indication that we were ready for a race. On the long stretch of road, we would squeal our tires, breaking free as soon as the challenge was accepted. Winning was everything. No boy wanted to lose to a car full of girls. Bragging rights were trophy enough for anyone who had the gumption to play. We all felt like we had so much to prove.

It seems like it was so long ago, what happened on the road that particular day. I'd always been told that the Bible says there is no greater gift than if a man lay down his life for a friend. That day, life was surely laid down. The accident changed me from a carefree girl to a careful young woman. In a moment's time, I understood what it truly meant to carry the burden of a friend, even if it meant possible death.

It was May of our junior year in high school, 1973. My best friend Laura and I spent a great deal of our time looking through fashion magazines and learning the words to every song on the billboard top-10 chart. I remember we had dreams of moving together to the "big city," driving a convertible, and being the envy of every girl in our high school that we could not stand. It was a good time cut way to short. That previous winter, Laura's mama had been diagnosed with cancer.

In those days, cancer was frequently a death sentence. There were not as many successful options then as there are now. Laura's mama refused the hope of chemotherapy. She chose to fight the enemy with only the time that she had left. With dignity and grace, she prepared for her end in the comfort of her own home. Laura's daddy was able to arrange for a nurse to come and administer the needed drugs to make her mama comfortable. Her slow descent toward her mortality was played out in their living room . . . the final act becoming a normal way of life for all of us.

I would visit Laura's home several times a week to show my support to her family. They lived in an old historic house that had a large Southern-style porch. When I arrived, Laura's mama would often be sitting on the porch swing taking in the fresh air.

"Hi," I tried to be upbeat when I spoke to her. I felt the need to be animated. I thought it would cheer her up.

"It's beautiful weather today . . . why, I don't ever remember seeing a sky so blue." The look in her eyes would be distant. She was cloudy in her thoughts from the medication.

"Do you know me today, Mrs. C?" The C was short for Constantine. We never called Laura's parents by their full last name.

She looked through me. Then she turned her head toward the house. "Laura's inside." She said it hollow, with no emotion. I smiled meekly, feeling uncomfortable.

"Oh, thanks . . . OK . . . inside." My fake cheeriness made me shake my head at myself. Thinking back on it, I realize there is no cheer in the face of death. But it's hard to know how to react. No one writes instruction booklets on how to make the dying smile.

Inside, the house would reek of what we called "cancer smell." I imagined it was a combination of medication, bile (Mrs. C. was constantly throwing up), and intravenous fluid. After you were inside for a minute, the odor became tolerable. We didn't have a choice but to adjust. It was what Mrs. C. wanted. She planned to go on with life as usual, right to the end. But of course, there was nothing usual about it and, in the long run, I think those who loved her suffered more watching her go through the pain than she could ever have imagined.

Laura was emotionally drained trying to deal with life. She hid her feelings deep down inside this seemingly bottomless well. The blatant pretending that nothing was wrong had been taking its toll for months. I knew that one day soon the denial in the well of emotion would rise to the top and it wouldn't just overflow, it would sprout like a geyser.

The final weeks passed quickly. Laura became despondent as her mama grew weaker. I wanted to talk to Laura about her mama many times but I didn't know how. So I resorted to "being there" In those moments of "being there," Laura would lay her head on my shoulder. There were no words. She would cry softly and I would pretend not to notice. As she wiped her tears away in silence, I prayed for her. My prayer was not what I thought it should be, and I admit I felt guilty. But someone had to pray it. That girl needed relief from the burden. And that's exactly what I prayed to God . . . *relieve her from this burden as soon as You can!*

There was an incident in school one day that finally led to Laura's eruption. There was a boy named Rory that Laura was madly in love with. Rory was in her biology class. He was a good friend of ours who we'd both known since grade school. The two of them discovered feelings for one another at Evelyn Barnwell's birthday party. Laura and Rory had really hit if off. Enter Janet Crosby, Rory's ex-girlfriend who was very unhappy to have the title of "ex."

Laura and Janet became fierce enemies with good reason. Each time Janet had the opportunity to corner Rory, she did just that, and right out in the open. Rory would tell her to leave him alone but she was determined. Rumors started flying like dragon kites about Rory's infidelity.

Laura never believed any of them. "Unless I see them clutched in a Harlequin embrace with my own eyes," Laura would scoff, "I won't believe it. Rory wants nothing to do with that crazy girl. Besides," she would always defend him, "Rory gets me. He would never hurt me like that."

Laura had come to school that day knowing that the end was near for her mama. She was on her way to biology class when she rounded the hall corner. There, on her locker, were Rory and Janet in a lip-lock. Laura dropped her books and took off running. I was standing at my locker when I heard the commotion. I turned to catch a glimpse of Laura running down the hall. Rory was yelling after her. I hurried past him.

"What did you do to her?" I pushed between him and Janet. She had a nasty little smirk on her face as if to say "mission accomplished."

I took off running after Laura. I was able to catch up to her just as she jumped into her father's old yellow Cadillac. She had borrowed the car for the day to run errands for her family after school. She started the ignition. I pulled the door open, dived in, and she took off.

Laura was frantic. She was driving reckless. I knew I had to say something.

"I'm sorry . . . he's a stupid jerk. He's not worth it."

She floored the accelerator. The speedometer hit 65. The speed limit was 25.

I begged her to slow down. "Girl," I joked nervously, "all we need is for your daddy to pull us over." Her daddy was an officer of the law. "We'd be grounded our entire senior year."

My attempts to make her laugh failed miserably. She hit a bump and it threw me against the door. I reached for my seatbelt and put it on. The speedometer hit 75. The car was rattling. I was getting scared. She didn't seem to notice that the car felt like it would fall apart. She just looked real mad.

"Please," I said, trying to remain calm, "slow down . . . talk to me . . . is it Rory? Is that what this is all about?"

Tears streamed down Laura's face. She looked as though she were going to do something desperate. We were on the back roads in the country now. She had driven so fast through downtown that she turned the 20-minute drive into 10. I was pleading with her unresponsiveness.

"You've got to talk about it . . . get it out," I yelled at her. "What's in your head?" That's when the geyser erupted.

"What's in my head? I just saw my supposed boyfriend kissing Janet Crosby . . . she's ugly and she cheats on him, but he'd still rather have her than me. My sister's out of control and I don't know how to handle her—no one can handle her, only mama can. She's the only one who has ever been able to control her. My brother cries himself asleep every night because he's so sad about mama, and so does daddy—I hear him in his room sometimes."

That really hit me hard. I couldn't see her daddy doing that, he always seemed so strong. I began to cry.

"Last night, she was so sick. I said 'mama, it's me Laura,' and she didn't know me. My mama didn't know me."

It was too much. Both of us were weeping. I tried to comfort her by putting my hand on her shoulder. It seemed like a pitiful gesture given the circumstances.

"I need her, oh, God, I need her . . . she can't leave us, she can't . . . what will we do?" Laura was sobbing as she wearily banged the steering wheel with both hands. The cancer had stolen so much from their lives. "I'm sick of trying to be everything to everyone. I can't do it anymore . . . I don't want anyone to depend on me. I'm just a kid . . . I want my life back."

Suddenly, I felt "stomach in the mouth syndrome." The valley of the country road had swooped us up at 80 miles per hour. We watched through our windows as the pavement dropped beneath us. When the car hit the road, its front wheels turned a hard right. Laura lost control. The car flipped twice.

I remember pushing open the car door. I was still strapped in tight. I unfastened the seatbelt and climbed out of the wreckage. I came to my senses for a moment and looked back over my shoulder into the car for Laura but she wasn't there. "Laura," I screamed. Blackness engulfed me as I fell head first to the ground.

I suffered only a minor concussion. Laura was thrown from the car and sustained a broken arm. She was mortified that the consequences of her actions could have resulted in our deaths. Everyone who saw the car told us how lucky we were to be alive. Everyone also told us that we should have known better. My own family, even though grateful we were all right, still scolded me for getting in the car with someone who was so distraught. Yes, we both knew. We should have used better common sense. But, then, after the fact, it really didn't matter. The most important thing was that we survived it together.

Laura and I learned how valuable our friendship was that day on the country road. Our sisterhood was true and that was worth more than anything at the time in our world. There was no one to blame. There was a great deal of understanding and healing that summer of 1973. It would always be a part of our life's journey that we shared, and a memory that we would never forget.

The following week after the incident, Laura's mama passed away. My family and I met Laura's family at their house before the funeral to express our condolences. When Laura saw me, she fell into my arms and cried. We never talked about the accident or about her mama's death. We didn't have to. I knew what she felt in her heart and there were no words to express it.

A few weeks after the funeral, Laura seemed almost her old self. There was a sense of sadness about her, but also a sense of relief. The following year, on my 17th birthday, she threw me a surprise party. When she came up to hug me, she smiled and whispered in my ear,

"We had the best ride on the road ever . . . happy birthday, girl." And because she was doing so well, it was one of the happiest ever.

Contributing Authors

Betty Wilson Beamguard

Betty Wilson Beamguard's publication credits include 34 stories, 10 poems, and numerous humorous essays. Three of her how-to articles have been featured in *The Writer* with a fourth scheduled. Her work has appeared in such publications as *Women in the Outdoors, Draft Horse Journal, Sasee, moonShine Review, Freckles to Wrinkles,* and *Sweet Tea and Afternoon Tales.* Betty's story, "Mercy for a Kitten," was chosen by the South Carolina Fiction Project in 2009. She lives near Clover, SC. Her new passion is paddling the waterways of North and South Carolina. Her website: www.home.earthlink.net/~bbeamguard

Paddy M. Bell

Paddy's first writing endeavor, *DOGS: The Musical,* was produced in three theatre venues, culminating in acceptance and a 12-show run at the Piccolo Spoleto Arts Festival in 2007. This success launched a writing interest that has resulted in a second play currently in development, *For You The War Is Over,* a World War II veteran's experiences paralleled with veterans from current-day conflicts. She has also written the libretto for a potential children's opera, *The True Adventures of the Billy Goats Gruff,* and has several illustrated children's books in the works.

Billie Bierer

Billie Bierer was born in Texas, grew up in Pennsylvania, and moved with her parents to Arizona in the 1960s. Being a flower child was out for her. As a teenager, she fell in love with the West and became a cowgirl. Married for 39 years, she and her husband raised three children. Now, the grandmother of six, she has settled in her husband's home state of South Carolina where they have Arabian horses. Billie is at work on her next novel, *Faster Horses* (working title). She has written many short stories. Her web site at www.billiebierer.com will keep you up to date with her latest news.

Kimberlyn Blum-Hyclak

Kimberlyn Blum-Hyclak lives in Lancaster, SC with her husband and the youngest of their five children. Kim's first nonfiction work was published in the 2008 issue of *The Petigru Review* and her poetry has been published in *The Petigru Review, Catfish Stew, Kakalak,* and *Iodine.* Her daughter Gabrielle, the subject of "Coming Home," recently celebrated her 24th birthday and has been in remission for 14 years.

Susan Boles

Susan Boles, a native North Carolinian, retired to Murrells Inlet, SC after a varied career that ended with teaching high school Spanish. When Susan took her first creative-writing class, she was hooked. Many of her happiest moments are spent with her laptop under the spell of spirited imagination. This is her third inclusion in *Petigru Review.* She has also published poems and nonfiction pieces *in Voices of the Low Country* and *Sasee.* She owes much to her local SCWW Writers Group and Wildacres Writers Workshop.

Dick Brook

Dick Brook is a long-term writer of fiction and nonfiction. From 1968 to the early 1980s, he was a contributing editor for the *North American Review.* His chief effort in fiction at the *NAR* included a Winter 1979 story entitled "Wanda's Wedding," a chapter from an unpublished novel called "Delaney's Arcade Bear." For more than 10 years, he was on the masthead of the *NAR* and was once responsible for "Books" or simply identified as a "Contributing Editor." During his time with the *NAR,* he chiefly did reviews and nonfiction articles, including a longish summary of myths from the future of higher education.

Donna Campbell
Donna Campbell grew up in Wagener, SC and earned an English degree from Clemson University. After many years of teaching language arts in New Jersey, she and her husband have returned to South Carolina where they now live in West Union. She is a member of the newly formed Oconee chapter of SCWW, a wonderful group of supportive writers. This is her fifth inclusion in the SCWW anthologies.

Kim Catanzarite
Kim Catanzarite is a freelance writer and editor who lives in Charleston with her husband and daughter. Her short fiction has appeared in *Emry's Journal, The Evansville Review,* and *moonShine review.* She is a two-time winner of the South Carolina Fiction Prize, and a winner of the Carrie McCray Literary Award for nonfiction. Last year, she was nominated for a Pushcart Prize.

Melinda Cotton
Melinda Cotton, born and raised in Columbia, SC, is a member of SCWW, Columbia Chapter One, where she receives positive feedback and propulsion to pursue her lifelong dream of writing. Her 20-year legal career recently landed her in the Department of Justice at the US Attorney's Office. Between her full-time job, husband, son, family, and friends, she finds it difficult to find time for her writing passion. Ironically, "No Time to Write" is her first publication. When the opportunity presents itself, she's hard at work on her first novel, a legal mystery set in Charleston, SC.

Matthew M. Devlin
Matthew M. Devlin is currently working toward his Bachelor of Arts in History. He has yet to choose an area of concentration, and currently has no leanings either way. In addition to being an epic procrastinator, he is also a member of SCWW. Not only does he write short stories, he also fancies himself a poet. His short story, "Morning," marks his first time in publication.

S. Jane Gari
After spending eleven years as a high school English teacher, S. Jane Gari is enjoying a hiatus to raise a daughter and write. She received her BA in English from SUNY at Stony Brook and her MA in English from New York University. Gari won the first-place Carrie McCray Memorial Literary Award for nonfiction at the 2008 SCWW Conference. Occasionally, you can hear her read poetry and prose pieces live at the Art Bar in Columbia. Besides politically and esoterically charged poetry, her other current projects include an irreverent bathroom reader and a nearly completed memoir.

Steve Gordy
Steve Gordy is a retired technical trainer and technical writer who is trying his hand at creative writing. His piece "Private Horrors" in this anthology is a snippet from his novel *Henry Gorlitz Is Dead*, which he is in the process of marketing to agents and publishers. Steve and his wife live in Aiken, SC and are looking forward to a retirement "on the road."

Tim Harkins

Tim Harkins retired from the Navy in 1995 and since has worked as a technical writer. His poems have been published in *PanGaia, newWitch,* the *Chrysalis Reader,* and the *Poetry Society of South Carolina Yearbook* for 2008 and 2009. His chapbook, *Chasing The Ineffable,* won the South Carolina Poetry Initiative Chapbook Contest in 2007 and was published by Stepping Stones Press in October 2008. Tim began writing poetry at age 13 when he really needed to impress the girl down the street. It didn't work, but he kept writing.

Steve Heckman

Steve Heckman lives and writes in the Dark Corner, in northern Greenville County. An engineer by training and a salesman by trade, he writes short stories and limericks, which he can usually finish, and a novel, which he cannot. He and wife Toni are empty-nesters who still make each other laugh after 30-some years.

Donna Higgons

Donna Higgons has published true tales of her adventures on land and sea in various national and local publications including *SAIL Magazine, Coastal Cruising Magazine, The Stowe* (Vermont) *Reporter,* and the *Stowe/Smugglers Notch Guide,* as well as writing newsletters and publicity for not-for-profit and for-profit organizations. She recently ventured into fiction writing and is currently working on a historical novel set in Eighteenth Century Maine. Donna lives in Sunset Beach, NC.

Gene Hines

Gene Hines (blaneyhines2@yahoo.com) is a legal-services attorney in Asheville, NC, representing victims of domestic violence. He confesses to writing the occasional horror story, but only when driven to it by one too many a tale from a domestic-violence victim. Otherwise, most of his stories have appeared in the proper literary journals.

Lynne M. Hinkey

Lynne Hinkey is a biology professor at Trident Technical College in Charleston, SC, and online for the University of Maryland-University College. After "donkey years" living in the Caribbean, she moved to South Carolina to work for NOAA. An opportunity to live in Germany for three years also provided her with the chance to pursue her long-time dream: writing. Lynne has had short stories, essays, and research articles published in newspapers, literary, and scientific journals. The short story "Paradise Found?" was derived from her novel-in-progress, *Marina Melee.*

Elsie Holcombe

Elsie lives in Anderson, SC. Her poetry and short stories have been recognized by *Foothills Writers, Catfish Stew, Writer's Digest Contest, the Quill, Arkansas Pen Women, Poetry Society of South Carolina,* and *The Petigru Review.* She was also recognized as a contender for *Kakalak.* Her love of the sea is expressed in a chapbook, *O' Tell Me Great Sea,* a series of quatrains written by her and illustrated by her daughter. Her latest poem, *"What if the World was Upside Down"* won first place in the children's category of *PSSC.* It is currently being published in a picture book for the small members of her family.

Millard R. Howington

Millard R. Howington joined the SCWW Aiken Chapter in 1994, and served as president of SCWW, 1996-1999. Retired now in New Ellenton, SC, he spends a great deal of his time trying to keep up with his two Jack Russell dogs. Like his father before him, he reads in the shade of his two Burford Holley trees, with berries that will turn red in the fall, and he goes to church twice on Sunday if it doesn't rain. He has always been grateful for SCWW, the things learned about the art of writing, and the fellowship of kindred spirits.

Kathryn Jeffcoat

Kathryn Jeffcoat is the mother of three, who has been quietly writing for a decade. She has a great love for the art of poetry and enjoys reading it, from the classic to the contemporary.

Will Jones

Will is a rascal. He works at a large research-and-development laboratory, where he's often mistaken for an engineer. To this he replies with a grin, "No. I'm a geologist. I have a sense of humor." His piece in this issue is dedicated to his grandmother, Erma Cantrell Jones, who is 105 years old. She and his other grandparents taught him the meaning of selflessness and honor through living those qualities daily. He is fortunate to have seen that tradition lived by his parents and his wife, and continued in the lives of his daughter and her husband.

Janet Sheppard Kelleher

Janet Sheppard Kelleher, a nine-year cancer victor, and her husband of 33 years look forward to their three children creating grandparents. After a lifetime of selling everything from ham hocks to houses, Jan prefers fishing, traveling, exploring antique shops, hunting, parasailing, studying her Bible, cooking, Scrabbling, crossword and Sudoku puzzling, reading, and lately, writing. The liberal-arts facet of Jan's

mathematics degree from Sweet Briar College is manifesting itself with short stories and a humorous Southern coming-of-age novel, *Sunshine, Moonshine & Spanish Moss/The Chest Beneath God's Beard*. Editing her manuscript to agent-worthiness is a consuming and exacting passion.

Robin Lewis

Robin Lewis began writing poetry as a child growing up on an isolated farm in rural West Virginia. Throughout her teen years, her work appeared many times in high-school literary magazines and local and state publications and was first published nationally in *Young Author's Magazine*. She also earned acclaim for her writing as a student at both Warren Wilson College and Massachusetts College of Liberal Arts, where she earned a degree in English and Creative Writing and won a 2004 fiction award. She now lives with her partner and daughter in coastal South Carolina where the landscape continues to delight and inspire her.

Grace W. Looper

Grace W. Looper writes all types of fiction. She has won awards from Southeastern Writers Conference, SCWW, and Charlotte Writer's Club. She has had stories published in the *Evening Herald, Touch Magazine, Charlotte Writers Annual Award Anthology, Catfish Stew,* and *The Rocking Chair Reader: Memories from the Attic.* The first three of a series has been published: *Molasses Making Time* (2004), *Great Grandpa's Hidden Treasure* (2006), and *A Call for Courage* (2009). She has completed the fourth and final book in the series, *A Second Chance.*

Kathryn Etters Lovatt

Kathryn Etters Lovatt holds an MA in Creative Writing from Hollins College. Her work has appeared in a number of journals and anthologies. She is a past winner of the Robert Ruark Award for short fiction and North Carolina Writers' Network's Doris Betts Fiction Prize. In 2007, editors of *The Petigru Review* nominated her story for a Pushcart Prize. She received SCWW's Carrie McCray Memorial Award for short fiction in 2008. She lives in Camden, SC.

Nan Lundeen

Nan Lundeen has published *The Pantyhose Declarations*, a collection of poems honoring Mother Earth in her many guises, including the robust women of her Iowa heritage, such as Aunt Geneva, who struggles like a sumo wrestler with her corset on her wedding day. Her poems have been published in several literary journals including The College of Charleston's *Illuminations*, and online by South Carolina Poetry Initiative and *The Iowa Review's* "Iowa Writes." A regular contributor to *The Petigru Review*, the Greer resident's work has been accepted by the University of South Carolina's *South Carolina Anthology*.

Richard Lutman

Richard Lutman has an MFA in Writing from Vermont College and has taught fiction and composition classes in Connecticut and Rhode Island. His fiction has been published in *Crazy Quilt, Verdad, Slow Trains,* and *The Newport Review*. He has also won awards for his short stories, nonfiction, and screenplays. He was a 2008 Pushcart Nominee. He currrently teaches short-story classes as part of Coastal Carolina University's Lifelong Learning program. A chapbook of his flash fiction was published in June from Last Automat Press.

Michael Hugh Lythgoe

Michael Hugh Lythgoe grew up in Indiana. He was educated at St. Louis University, the University of Notre Dame, and Bennington College (MFA). Mike is a retired Air Force officer who has worked as a foundation director, teacher, and college administrator. He is president of the Aiken Choral Society. He has poems and reviews forthcoming in *Windhover, Praesidium,* and *The Art of Peace* (a chapbook anthology to be published by Fordham University). He lives with his wife, Louise, in Aiken.

Jim McFarlane

Jim McFarlane creates computer applications for a chemical company that has experienced five name changes and American, German, and Japanese ownership in the past 30 years. His goal is to publish a book that his daughter can sell in her used-and-new bookstore in Greenville, SC.

Missy Nicholson

Missy Nicholson was born and raised in what she's sure is the Center of the Universe—Greer, SC. She is happily married to her high school sweetheart, Nick, and they are gingerly traversing the teenage years with two daughters, Mary Kate and Zoe. Two dogs and a bad-tempered cat allow them to share the house. Missy enjoys reading, writing, beachcombing, and volunteering.

Valerie Keiser Norris

Valerie Keiser Norris has been telling and writing stories for as long as she can remember. Her publication credits include short stories (one of them a humorous story for *Golf Digest*), articles, poems, and several contests and awards. She grew up in Michigan with scads of siblings, cousins, aunts and uncles, and was dragged to Georgia by her husband who thought a steady income was more important than family connections. Twenty-one years later they moved to South Carolina to be nearer to daughters and grandkids. She hopes she's accepted because she's not leaving! Valerie is currently working on a humorous novel.

Robin O'Bryant

Robin O'Bryant is a columnist for *The Moultrie News* in Mount Pleasant, SC. She writes a weekly humor column based on her life as a mother to three young daughters. She also writes a column for *Christian Ladies Connect,* a bimonthly online magazine. Robin is the creator of www.robinschicks.com, a website devoted to documenting the hilarity and madness of her life and as a member of the Charleston chapter of SCWW. She has recently signed with literary agent Jenny Bent and is in the process of completing her first book, a collection of non-fiction humor.

Trilby Plants

Trilby Plants has been captivated by stories since she was five, when her mother read her *Gulliver's Travels*. Plants, a lifelong storyteller and poet, shared her love of reading and writing with others as a teacher and a published author of fiction and poetry. She has two adult children who share her fascination with words: her son makes his living writing, and her daughter is an actor. Besides telling the stories that clamor to be told, Plants is a digital scrapbook designer and plays as much golf as possible with her husband—who is also a voracious reader.

Charles P. Reeve

Charles P. Reeve is a retired statistician living in Aiken with his wife of 40 years. In addition to writing, he enjoys golf, chess, and photography. He has been a member of SCWW since 1998.

Brenda Bevan Remmes

Brenda retired in 2005 after 30 years in education, which began with the Peace Corps in Cameroon, West Africa, in 1969. While most of her prior writing was on curricula and grants for health education, she turned her attention to exploring the attics and letters of her colorful ancestors and published the book *Everything Happens at the Crossroads* in 2008. Excerpts from the book recently appeared in the *USC Caroliniana Columns* magazine. She is now working on her first novel. She lives with her husband in the Salem Black River Community of South Carolina. Their two sons have successfully launched.

Sally Arango Renata

A California transplant by way of Colorado and Connecticut, Sally Arango Renata has lived in Surfside Beach for 15 years. A writer and folk artist, her work has appeared in publications including *The Petigru Review, The Shine Journal, Joyful!, ken*again,* and *FM Aware.* Renata's work has placed in the competitive Interboard Poetry Competition. She helped edit *The Writers' Circle Anthology,* has judged poetry competitions, was a 2007 Horry County ACE grantee, was named 2008-2009 Poetry Fellow by the South Carolina Arts Commission, is listed in the Southern Arts Registry, and is a Pushcart Prize nominee. Life is the fodder of her writing.

Martha T. Robinson

Martha T. Robinson is a special-education teacher in Rock Hill, SC. In her spare time, she loves to read and write poems, flash fiction, and personal essays. Her work has been published in *Mom Writers Literary Magazine, moonShine review, Petigru Review,* and *Catfish Stew.*

Maureen Sherbondy

Maureen Sherbondy's fiction has appeared in *The North Carolina Literary Review, moonShine Review, Stone Canoe*, and in the anthology (Knoxville Writers' Guild) *Low Explosions: Writings on the Body*. A story was a finalist in Southeast Review's Best Short-Short Story Contest. A story was also selected as a runner-up in the William Faulkner William Wisdom Creative Writing Contest. Maureen's chapbook, *After the Fairy Tale*, was published by Main Street Rag in 2007. A second chapbook, *Praying at Coffee Shops*, was published in 2008. Her short-story collection, *The Slow Vanishing*, will be published in the fall.

Marilyn N. Smith

Marilyn Smith, the great-granddaughter of homesteading pioneers, was born on the high plains of southwestern Kansas and has lived in the Midwest, the Caribbean, the New Mexican desert, and in Europe before settling in the Lowcountry of South Carolina. In each of these settings, she has collected material for her poems. She now lives and writes in Beaufort, SC.

Bob Strother

Forty years in government honed Bob Strother's cynicism, heightened his appreciation for irony, and gave birth to a new career in creative writing. His short fiction has been published in more than a dozen literary journals and he has just completed work on a fourth novel. In 2008, his short story, "Silent Prayer," was nominated for The Pushcart Prize. Serving on the SCWW Board of Directors allows him the opportunity to grow professionally and encourage the development of new writers. Bob's web address is www.bobstrother.net.

Brittany Vandeputte

Brittany Vandeputte is an award-winning playwright who lives and writes in Greenville, SC. When she isn't writing, she enjoys embroidery, doll making, and being mom to her two young sons. Visit her blog at www.brittanyvandeputte.blogspot.com.

David F. Westeren

David F. Westeren grew up in coastal Rhode Island. He received a BA in English from the University of Rhode Island and an MAT from Rhode Island College. Since the late Seventies, he has lived in the American South. His short stories and poems have been included in science-fiction and regional literary anthologies. He lives in Columbia, SC and is at work on a novel.

Lisa Wright-Dixon

Lisa Wright-Dixon received her Bachelor of Arts degree from Syracuse University. Her passions include her husband of 15 years, Gregory, and their six cats: Milo-Gray Davis, Miss Kayley Ann Marie, Boomer LeeAnn, Jasmine Marie, Tigeroo, and the baby, Lola Ally-Marie. She enjoys reading, writing, working out, and life. She recently had her first story published in *Chicken Soup for the Soul: Tough Times, Tough People*. Lisa resides in Aiken, South Carolina where she is currently working on a book of childhood memoirs as well as actively seeking a publisher. E-mail her at author-author@earthlink.net.

Competition Judges

Anne C. Barnhill

Anne C. Barnhill's short-story collection, *What You Long For*, will be published in May 2009, by *Main Street Rag* and her work has appeared in a number of literary magazines and anthologies including, most recently, *The Antietam Review* and *Racing Home: New Stories from Award-Winning North Carolina Writers*. Other publications include the story, "Washing Helen's Hair," from the Grammy-nominated anthology *Grow Old Along With Me,* and "The Swing," from *Generation to Generation*. She has received an Emerging Artist Grant, a Regional Artist Grant, and a writer's residency at the Syvenna Foundation in Texas. She has been selected as a Blumenthal Reader twice and her stories have won several awards, including the Porter Fleming Fiction Award from the Augusta, Georgia Arts Council.

Barnhill publishes nonfiction with a variety of newspapers and magazines, including *Our State Magazine: Down Home In North Carolina*. Her book reviews have appeared in *The Notre Dame Review, Main Street Rag*, the *Winston Salem Journal,* and the *Greensboro News and Record*.

Her memoir, *At Home in the Land of Oz: Autism, My Sister and Me,* from Jessica Kingsley Publishers in London, tells the story about what it was like growing up with her autistic sister, Rebecca. Clyde Edgerton says this about the book:

> Anne Barnhill, in *At Home in the Land of Oz,* has written a story that deserves a far brighter and higher billing than the kind of easy, happy, feel-good non-fiction that often tops the best-seller lists. This is because her story deals with those quiet heroics that many families and individuals face while they hide away in pain and misunderstanding. In facing autism full on, Ms. Barnhill has demonstrated how humans can love each other in unspeakable ways, learning languages as well as contours of certain rooms of the heart that some of us are never fortunate enough to know.

And Fred Chappell adds:

> . . . A story filled with suspense, humor, empathy, frustration, triumph and heartbreak. Anne Barnhill writes economically, cleanly and frankly and her words will go to the heart of every reader. From her pages I learned that endurance can be the most important component of courage, and I learned in a most entertaining way.

Ms. Barnhill has been the keynote speaker at meetings of Episcopal Church Women in North Carolina and South Carolina. She has also presented programs about memoir writing at Converse College, the Kernersville Moravian Church, the Kernersville Library Book Club, and other book clubs. She has taught memoir writing and fiction writing in a variety of places, including: Guilford College, Greensboro, NC; University of North Carolina at Greensboro; Guilford Technical Community College; the Phoenix Festival at High Point University; and the Greensboro YMCA for Seniors. She has also taught courses in creativity for the faculty and staff at Guilford College and the Center for Creative Leadership, both in Greensboro. She holds an MFA in Creative Writing from UNC-Wilmington and is currently at work on a novel set in Tudor England.

A.J Hartley

British-born writer A.J. Hartley got his first taste for archaeology touring sites in Greece and Rome as a child with his family. As an English major at Manchester University, he took extra classes in Egyptology and got a job working on a Bronze Age site just outside Jerusalem. Since then, life has taken him to many places around the world—including a couple of years in Japan—and though he always leaned more toward the literary than to the strictly historical, his fascination with the past has continued unabated. He is the *USA Today* and *New York Times* bestselling author of the mystery/thrillers *The Mask of Atreus*, and *On the Fifth Day,* which have been printed in 20 languages worldwide. His third thriller, *What Time Devours*, which centers on a lost Shakespeare play, was released by Penguin/Berkley in January 2009. His first fantasy adventure, *Act of Will* (starred review in Publishers Weekly), was published by Tor/Macmillan in March 2009.

A.J. has an MA and Ph.D in English literature from Boston University and is currently the Distinguished Professor of Shakespeare in the Department of Theatre at the University of North Carolina at Charlotte. He is the director of the Shakespeare in Action Centre, the editor of the performance journal *Shakespeare Bulletin* published by Johns Hopkins UP, and the author of *The Shakespearean Dramaturg* as well as numerous articles in the field. He is currently writing a performance history of *Julius Caesar* for Manchester UP.

As well as being a novelist and academic, he is a screenwriter, theatre director, and dramaturg. He makes beer and furniture and has more hobbies than is good for anyone. He is married with a son, and lives in Charlotte.

Derek Nikitas

Derek Nikitas's first novel, *Pyres* (St. Martin's Minotaur, 2007) earned an Edgar Award nomination. His second novel, *The Long Division,* was released in October 2009 (St. Martin's Minotaur). He has published stories in *The Ontario Review, Ellery Queen Mystery Magazine, Chelsea, Thuglit, The Pedestal Magazine,* and other venues. He was a 2007 Fellow at the Sewanee Writers Conference and has been nominated for a Pushcart award. His MFA in Creative Writing is from UNC-Wilmington and he teaches creative writing in the MFA program at Eastern Kentucky University.

NONFICTION:

Kay B. Day

Independent journalist Kay B. Day writes the "Web Savvy" column for *The Writer* and hosts her own column at *The US Report*. Day has won awards for nonfiction, fiction, and poetry. The author of three books with a fourth about to be published, Day has contributed to a number of anthologies like *The Writer's Handbook, Letters to the World,* and *Faces of Freedom.* She has provided articles and analyses to *Sky News, The Florida Times Union, United Press International, Christian Science Monitor, Newsmax,* and dozens of other publications and websites. She speaks frequently to writing groups, colleges, and trade associations about her experiences. She has interviewed the person on the street as well as celebrities like Ken Burns and Russell Crowe. Day is a member of the American Society of Journalists and Authors and The Authors Guild. A native of South Carolina, she resides in Jacksonville, Florida.

Sheila R. McKinney

Sheila R. McKinney enjoyed a 25-year career with the *Chronicle-Independent,* a tri-weekly newspaper in Camden, SC. Having been "Localife" editor since 1986, she reported on a wide variety of community activities, including arts and entertainment, individual and organizational achievements, and church and civic projects. Among her numerous awards from the South Carolina Press Association were those for feature writing, critical writing, lifestyle section, and page design.

Since her retirement from the *Chronicle-Independent* in January 2006, she has written occasional articles for the newspaper, as well as several for various organizations, including three about the Fine Arts Center of Kershaw County's annual spring festival, Jazz at the Center, which have been published in *Just Jazz Guitar* magazine.

As she strives to bring the reader into the scene in a feature story, she also enjoys bringing the written word to life on the stage. Through the years, she has played principal roles with The Actors' Theatre of South Carolina and the Camden Community Theatre. Since her retirement from the newspaper, she has fulfilled a longtime goal to play Amanda Wingfield in Tennessee Williams's *The Glass Menagerie.*

Currently, Mrs. McKinney serves on the Fine Arts Center of Kershaw County Board of Directors.

Lisa Annelouise Rentz

Lisa Annelouise Rentz lives and works in Beaufort. She is the editor of *ArtNews* magazine, a print publication of the Arts Council of Beaufort County, and the instigator of Iodine Literary Projects at www.eatgoodbread.com, including the Piccolo Fiction Open in Spoleto. Her work has been published by *Charleston* magazine, *The Lowcountry,* Salon.com, *night rally, Skirt, Yikes,* and *The Gullah Sentinel.* She is currently collaborating with dancer Caroline Hoadley on *The Carolina Shag: the Spirit of Southern Social Dance,* due out this year. When she works with teachers and students in Beaufort County schools, she defines creative writing as any writing that is not boring.

POETRY:

Darnell Arnoult

Darnell Arnoult's novel *Sufficient Grace* was published both in hardcover (2006) and paperback (2007) by Free Press, an imprint of Simon & Schuster, and was produced in unabridged audio by Recorded Books (2007). A Book Sense annual book-club-list selection, *Sufficient Grace* was nominated for the 2007 SIBA Fiction Book of the Year and 2006 Weatherford Award nominee.

What Travels With Us: Poems, published by Louisiana State University Press (2005), was named 2006 SIBA Poetry Book of the Year and won the 2005 Weatherford Award in Appalachian Literature, given by Berea College and the Appalachian Studies Association.

Arnoult's short fiction and poetry have appeared in a variety of journals including *Nantahala Review, Southern Cultures, Southwest Review, Southern Exposure, Asheville Poetry Review, Sandhills Review, Brightleaf, Now and Then Magazine*, and *Appalachian Heritage*. Her poetry has been featured by Garrison Keillor on *Writer's Almanac*.

With more than 17 years of teaching experience in creative writing and creative practice, Arnoult is a regular faculty member of the Duke Writers Workshop, Tennessee Young Writers Workshop, John C. Campbell Folk School, and Learning Events. She teaches fiction and poetry at conferences all over the Southeast. In 2007, Arnoult was named Tennessee Writer of the Year by the Tennessee Writers Alliance, and she is the 2009 recipient of the Mary Frances Hobson Prize in Arts and Letters.

Arnoult holds a BA in American Studies with a concentration in Southern Folklore from University of North Carolina at Chapel Hill and MA in English and Creative Writing from North Carolina State University. She is currently at work on her second novel and a new collection of poems while she completes her MFA in Creative Writing at the University of Memphis.

Mike Smith

Mike Smith was born in the mountain town of Philippi, WV, grew up in Greensboro, NC, and now lives near Raleigh with his young daughter and son. He holds degrees from UNC-G, Hollins College, and the University of Notre Dame, and served, most recently, as Writer-in-Residence at American University. He has published three chapbooks, including *Anagrams of America*, which is permanently archived at *Mudlark: Electronic Journal of Poetry and Poetics*, and has been nominated for the Pushcart Prize four times. He was an inaugural winner of the South Carolina Poetry Initiative's Poetry Chapbook Contest in 2006. He has had poems appear in the *Carolina Quarterly, Gulf Stream, The Iowa Review, The North American Review*, and *The Notre Dame Review*. His first full-length collection, *How to Make a Mummy*, was published in 2008. His second collection, *Multiverse*, will be published this January by BlazeVOX Books (Buffalo, NY).

Patricia Smith

Patricia Smith is the author of five books of poetry, including *Blood Dazzler*, chronicling the tragedy of Hurricane Katrina, which was a finalist for the 2008 National Book Award and one of NPR's top five books of 2008; and *Teahouse of the Almighty*, a National Poetry Series selection, winner of the Hurston-Wright Legacy Award and About.com's Best Poetry Book of 2006. She also authored the groundbreaking history *Africans in America* and the award-winning children's book *Janna and the Kings*. Her work has appeared in *Poetry, The Paris Review, TriQuarterly* and many other journals, and has been performed around the world, including Carnegie Hall, the Poets Stage in Stockholm, Rotterdam's Poetry International, the Aran Islands International Poetry and Prose Festival, the Bahia Festival, the Schomburg Center, and on tour in Germany, Austria, and Holland. She is a Pushcart Prize winner, a Cave Canem faculty member and a four-time individual champion of the National Poetry Slam, the most successful poet in the competition's history. She is on the faculty of the Stonecoast MFA program at the University of Southern Maine.

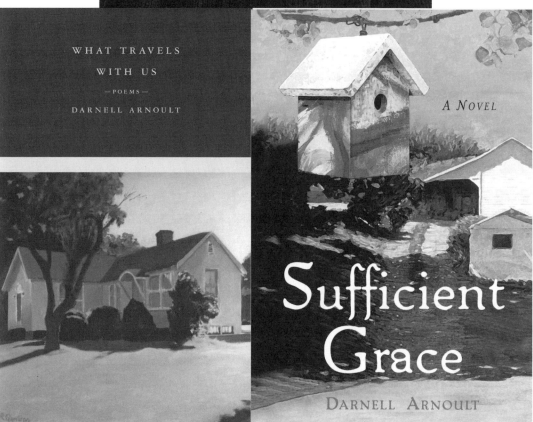

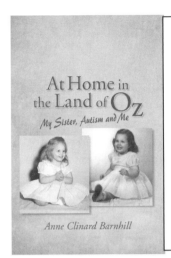

HER SISTER'S KEEPER

A Bittersweet Memoir About Growing Up With An Autistic Sister in the Sixties.

What You Long For, Stories
By Anne Clinard Barnhill,
forthcoming from Main Street Rag

What You Long For, by Anne Clinard Barnhill, is a rich collection that will make you laugh out loud in some places and cry in others. Filled with humor and tenderness, Barnhill has written an enormously entertaining group of stories. Whether she is describing country women telling one another stories in "The Quilting Bee," or introducing a little boy in love with his best friend's beer-drinking mother in "Kings and Damsels," Anne Barnhill creates unforgettable characters who feel like people you have encountered in your own life. She describes the interior life of women, in particular, with honesty and wonderfully real details from ordinary life. Simultaneously erotic and down-to-earth, *What You Long For* is bound to become a Southern classic.

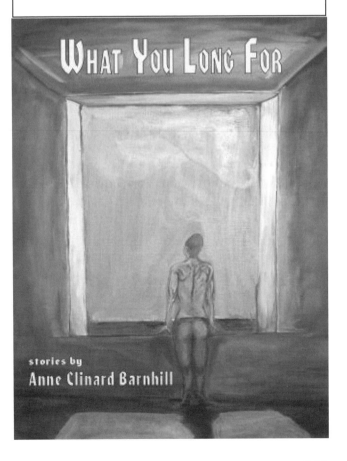

Do You Know Where Your Content Is?
By Kay B. Day

Write long enough and it will happen to you. A few months ago, a website published an article I had posted on my blog. I sent an e-mail requesting that they remove my content. They complied and sent an apology. One week later, the same website did it again. I e-mailed again. Only this time, I explained the legal ramifications. I knew from the look of the site that the owner was grabbing content so he could collect revenue from third-party advertisements.

I try to make time to see who is publishing my work. My column is syndicated, so I'm very particular about that content. But a website doesn't necessarily have to purchase my column to use it. If a blogger only uses an excerpt and includes a back link, that is appropriate and done in accordance with fair use.

It's a good idea to track of where your work is published. For one thing, you want to protect your brand. For another, if you're editing a commercial site with ads included, your own revenue will be diluted if someone uses your content illegally with the sole purpose of making money for himself. Finally, if the offending site has paid for placement and that site is higher in search-engine returns, your own rank may be penalized.

What can you do?

For starters, be sure you have a clear copyright policy posted somewhere on your website. A simple copyright symbol alongside your name and the year are good, but I always add the words, "all rights reserved." I also include a widget that links directly to the company that syndicates my content. Beneath the widget, I inserted several lines of copy explaining that use of more than a 250-word excerpt must go through the syndicate or a request must be sent to me.

The Web is bursting with content, so it's no surprise that the marketplace is responding to writers and other creatives who want to protect their work. The Fair Syndication Consortium will track content usage for you. There is no fee to join the FSC; you supply the URL of your feed to get reports about publication of your works. Another service, iCopyright, also tracks usage. Fees depend on the package you select.

There's also a homespun method for discovering where your work appears. A couple times a month, I select my top-ranked article and insert the whole first paragraph into a search engine. Last week, I discovered a very nice mention of a Web Savvy article that way, and the selected quotes were done in accordance with fair use. I was happy to see our work noted on the website because it was a quality site.

If you're writing for more than a hobby, tracking who has your content is smart for your bank account and your brand.

"As 18-year-old orphaned actor Will Hawthorne explains early on in this clever page-turner, "I don't want you thinking you're going to get a tale about some blue-eyed tyke with a heart of gold in a world where good triumphs over evil. You're not, I'm not, and in my experience it never does." Charged as a rebel after escaping the authorities in a world not unlike Elizabethan England, obnoxious, charming Will joins a small mercenary group and proves himself the least honorable of them all. When the group comes under attack from crimson-armored raiders, Will reluctantly fails to betray the companions he is even more reluctantly growing to like. In small, swift "scenes," Hartley (*On the Fifth Day*) deftly proves that people you shouldn't trust at your back can be the best ones to have at your side." (Mar.) Starred Review—Publishers Weekly 1.5.2009

Shelia R. McKinney

During my 20 years as "Localife" (lifestyle) editor at the *Chronicle-Independent* in Camden, SC, reams of work by aspiring writers landed on my desk. The authors hoped for an article, review, or mention of their literary efforts in the newspaper. Most of them were self-published novels, memoirs, poetry, or historical volumes. Most were less than compelling. Most needed more editing. Some were really bad. Some were surprisingly good.

So, when I was asked to judge the nonfiction category for *The Petigru Review*, I thought, "This might be interesting." I had no idea it would be such a pleasure. The only difficulty was making final decisions.

I was prepared for the possibility of dry, esoteric essays. That was definitely not the case. I was impressed by the quality, creativity, and diversity of the stories.

Sidney J. Palmer, Portraits Plus, Columbia, SC

For example, "The Shoebox" is an innovative illustration of how deeply divorce affects children, even adult children who are successfully going on with their lives. The author used wonderful verbs and imagery to help convey her emotions.

"A Sudden Man" records the relationship of a wise father, willing to learn from his grown son, as they strengthen their bond on a rugged mountain expedition.

"Sudden Death" and "Coming Home" are both thought-provoking explorations of coping with serious illness and death.

Then, there are the funny ones: "Christmas Gift," written in third person, has a great lead and a delightful turn in the plot. "Anything for a Story" creates a comical scene I can visualize in a movie, and "Watch Out" made this overly cautious judge laugh out loud. Good luck with your literary journal!

Coming from Minotaur Books, October, 27, 2009, is *The Long Division* by Derek Nikitas.

From the Edgar-nominated author of *Pyres* comes a novel of broken lives, long divided, now reunited in a frenzy of shocking events. . . .

Western New York sheriff's deputy Sam Hartwick secretly tracks the shooter in a double-murder case that will test his reputation and his faith in redemption. . . .

Jodie Larkin, an Atlanta housecleaner, fed up with her thankless job, hits the road with stolen cash, desperate to reconnect with the son she gave up for adoption. . . .

Wynn Johnston, a college student gifted and tortured, clings to his bright prospects while hunted by vengeful criminals, police, and his own demons. . . .

Inhibited Erika Hartwick battles her mother's relentless illness and gambles all her feelings on her father's worst nightmare. . . .

Calvin Nowak, a teenager eager to escape a family that could never understand his heart, hits the road on a runaway quest to discover the source of his pain. . . .

Past sins and present gambits will ensnare them all as they fight to keep from losing the only thing that makes them human: their souls.

"Coming off one of the most accomplished debuts in recent years, Derek Nikitas's second novel, *The Long Division,* exceeds even the grandest of expectations. As he deftly weaves together three perilous storylines, we feel ourselves simultaneously moved, horrified and brokenhearted as the novel spirals towards its breathtaking conclusion. Nikitas finds beauty and pathos in the smallest of gestures, the largest of actions, the darkest of paths. Not to be missed."

Lisa Annelouise Rentz

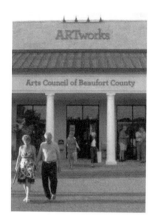

ARTworks is the home of the Arts Council of Beaufort County, in Beaufort Town Center: ArtNews magazine, now publishing fiction • recipient of the SC Humanities award for Literary Arts Advocacy • gallery shows & emerging artists • black box theater • MarshClass intensives, combining art-making & learning with the eco-magical Lowcountry landscape • working artists in their on-view studios • 4th Friday ARTjamz • Community Arts Grants for Beaufort County residents • the Ever Expanding Arts Calendar, online at

beaufortcountyarts.com

HOME OF ARTS COUNCIL OF BEAUFORT COUNTY

Mike Smith

It has been a great pleasure to serve as a poetry judge for the 2009 issue of *The Petigru Review*. The decision of which 20 poems to choose was hard enough, but the ranking of the poems proved very difficult, indeed. My love of poetry began with the reading of well-crafted work much like the poems I found in my large stack of contending entries. It is gratifying to come across strong evidence of love of process and craft; and it is humbling to realize how many of us persist in contending with the large questions of our time, which are, I suppose, not so different from the large questions of any other time. The contributors to this volume ought to be celebrated, also, for the wide range of approaches employed in the composition of these poems, surely testament to the liveliness of the South Carolina poetry scenes. I lived in Spartanburg, SC for three years in the early part of our current decade, so I've known for a while some of what I'm saying now.

Editors

Kevin Coyle

Kevin has been a member of the South Carolina Writers workshop since 2002, and has served on the SCWW Board of Directors as its Vice President. He is the proud father of two wonderful boys, Matthew and Michael. He divides his spare time between practicing law, writing novels and short stories, and acting in film and television. His Website: www.kevincoyle.net.

Phil Arnold

Phil's written works have been selected for the SCWW literary journal 14 of the last 15 years, including 13 essays, six short stories, and five poems. He is a past President of the Greenville Chapter and has served two terms on the SCWW Board of Directors. Phil's true love is writing about Elvis Presley. He now calls himself America's Most Prolific Elvis Writer by virtue of his 32 published articles in *Elvis . . . The Magazine* and 309 weekly articles posted on his blog, ElvisBlog (www.elvisblog.net), which receives more than 5,000 hits each week.

Kami Kinard

Kami's poetry, fiction, and nonfiction pieces have appeared in periodicals for both children and adults. Her first two books, both from *The Adventures of Dreadlock Jones* series that she created, are forthcoming in 2011 from G.P. Putnam's Sons. A teaching artist on the South Carolina Arts Commission's approved roster of artists, Kami lives with her family in Beaufort SC. More information about her work is available at www.kamikinard.com and at her newly created blog for people like her who need to exercise (but really don't want to) at www.hotpinkbike.wordpress.com.

SUPPORT INDEPENDENT BOOKSELLERS

THE FOLLOWING INDEPENDENT BOOKSELLERS IN SOUTH CAROLINA SPONSOR THE PETIGRU REVIEW. PLEASE SHOW YOUR APPRECIATION FOR THEIR GENEROUS SUPPORT BY SHOPPING WITH THEM.

LOWCOUNTRY:

Bookends
753 Main Street
North Myrtle Beach, SC 29582
(843) 280-2444
www.bookendsonline.com

Litchfield Books
14427 Ocean Highway, Unit G
Litchfield Landing
Pawleys Island, SC 29585
(843) 237-8138
www.litchfieldbooks.com

MIDLANDS:

Dr. Books
The Five Points Book Shop
718 Santee Avenue
Columbia, SC 29205
(803) 799-7182
www.abebooks.com/home/DRBooks

Ed's Editions
406 Meeting Street
West Columbia, SC 29169
(803) 791-8002
(866) 791-8002 (toll free)
www.edseditions.com

UPSTATE:

As the Page Turns
5000 Old Buncombe Road
Greenville, SC 29617
(864) 294-0122

Fiction Addiction
1020A Woodruff Road
Greenville, SC 29607
(864) 675-0540
www.fiction-addiction.com

J & S Books
P.O. Box 1164
Anderson, SC 29622
(864) 254-1262
www.jandsbooks.com

The Open Book
110 South Pleasantburg Drive
Greenville, SC 29607
(864) 235-9651
www.theopenbookonline.com